Beating
OVEReating

Beating
OVEReating

Riley
LONDON

www.eatingless.com

© Gillian Riley 2001, 2009

First published in 2001 by Gill & Macmillan, Dublin
New edition published in 2009 by Riley, London

Illustration by Judy Warner
Printed and bound by Russell Press, Nottingham

This book has been printed on 100% recycled paper.

ISBN: 978-0-9561051-0-3

CONTENTS

INTRODUCTION

THREE QUESTIONS

Welcome to an extraordinary journey. This will be an adventure, and just like all adventures it will be challenging, risky and full of surprises. At times you might think you'll never get anywhere and that nothing will ever change. At other times you might fear so much will change you won't be able to handle it. Just stay with it and watch what happens. Let those thoughts and fears come and go. Get some support with it if you want to, someone to talk to about it all. I know you want something to change; otherwise you wouldn't be reading this book in the first place. So you've already started the journey. Just don't give up on it, however long it takes, and you will get there in the end.

First things first. You want to change something about the way you are with food, so that you can be more in control of what you eat. Now, in order to change your actions, you change the way you think. Why? Because behind every action there's always a thought. The thought can be ever so subtle, so subtle you may not even notice it, but it's there. You think, 'Another slice of cake looks good' and before you know it you've eaten it. What you can do here is to learn a new way of thinking so that you can change your actions. Then, you have the opportunity not to eat that other slice of cake.

When it comes to changing the way you think about food, there are just three things to keep in mind. Let's call them themes. I'm going to describe what they are, so you can understand and remember them. Then, whenever your eating is not what you would like it to be – you're eating too much or maybe too much of the wrong things – you ask yourself about these three themes.

Whenever any one of them is out of place, you'll feel out of control with food in some way. You'll be eating too much or too often or the wrong things at the wrong times. When you question yourself about these three themes and find the truth about them for yourself, then you'll be able to gain control of your overeating. Then, you can feel at peace with food. Then, you have a good relationship with food. Then, willpower is an asset you naturally employ when it comes to what you eat.

So what are the three themes? I'll list them here and then I'll go into more detail over the following chapters:

1. AM I CHOOSING?   It's tough to stay in control of overeating if you don't know you've got the freedom to do whatever you want. If you ever notice a rebellious quality to your eating, especially if you feel completely out of control at times, this is the theme for you to tackle. If you keep putting off making good changes or if you feel deprived when you don't eat something, this is the theme for you. When you learn how to eliminate these problems, then you take control. Then you can make genuine choices that really work for you, using the power of your free will.

2. WHY DOES IT MATTER?   Here we look at why you might make one choice over any other. For example, you might ask yourself, 'Why don't I eat some more cake?' Or, 'Why am I snacking on an apple instead of a bar of chocolate?' We always have reasons for the things we do but often we lose sight of what they are, and this is very important when it comes to making lasting changes in what you are eating on a regular basis. In Chapter 2 we'll see how your motivation can be made much more powerful and sustainable.

3. HOW AM I RESPONDING TO TEMPTATION? This theme addresses your desire to overeat; the urge, impulse and attraction toward all that food you don't really need. In the past you may have tried to control this by distracting yourself, keeping

occupied with something else so that you don't feel tempted. But temptation rarely leaves for ever, so your success gets compromised. You can begin to think differently about feeling tempted and about feeling satisfied. When you do, the magic really starts to happen. This book shows you how.

Is it really this simple? Well, yes and no. It is simple in that all you need to remember is to question yourself about these three themes. It isn't simple in that you need to be honest with yourself so that you don't deceive yourself with false answers. A counsellor – anyone who can listen to you in a supportive way and give you straight and honest feedback – can help. It takes time, effort and courage to change the way you think, but it really is possible. And you can go as fast or as slow as you like.

WHAT YOU CAN DO

▸ Keep it private. Over the next few chapters you'll see how to develop a powerful and very practical sense of choice about food. When you start practising with these ideas, it's best to keep it to yourself as much as you possibly can. Think about this by yourself, without explaining or discussing what you're doing as part of your everyday conversations. Talking to a counsellor, support person or support group is fine, but as much as possible keep all your discussions about eating and weight within those designated meetings and conversations.

This advice goes double if you have someone in your life who puts any pressure on you to control your overeating and lose weight. If there's someone who makes comments about your size or comments on what you eat, that is especially the person you don't want to get involved in what you're learning here. They may well continue to make their comments but you don't have to respond to them, so don't take the bait and try to change the subject whenever you can.

Of course you'll need to make some decisions with others sometimes: what the family will have for dinner, perhaps, or what restaurant your group of friends will go to. But exactly what and how much you eat is up to you and is best decided by you. So, for example, if you want a second helping of something, you don't talk about it. You learn how to think it through for yourself and make a private decision about whether or not to have it.

This can be tough to do if you are used to talking with others about what you are or are not eating. You'll need to train your friends and family, to get them used to the new you who isn't going to think out loud about food and how you feel about eating or not eating it.

Later on, when you've spent a while working with this book, you may want to talk about some of it with people close to you. You'll know when you're ready to do that, and you'll know by then that it's still best not to talk about it when you are eating.

▸ Keep it simple. One of the best things about this approach is that you don't need to make other changes in your daily life in order for this to work. Taking control of overeating doesn't depend on whether you have a wildly exciting social life or are lonely and isolated. It doesn't depend on whether you're standing up, sitting down, watching TV or reading. It doesn't depend on whether you're at work or at home. Unemployed or bringing up children. Happy and productive or depressed and bored.

You can learn how to control what and how much you eat no matter what is going on in your life. And the best thing about this is that you don't need to wait until other things in your life change before you can make changes in your eating. You can get to work on it right way, just as things are. In fact, working on things just as they are right now is probably the best way to proceed. You'll see why later on in the book.

▸ Let it in. The first time you read this book you'll begin to understand the principles, but you're only going to get good results if you can let these ideas become real to you. It may take reading this book a couple of times before some of it begins to sink in enough to make a difference. This doesn't mean you are a slow learner or that you will never learn anything here that will really make a difference. It's just the way it is for most people. It takes a while, and this means you need to be a bit persistent. First of all you understand these themes, but then you need to live them by bringing them into the daily thoughts you have about food.

It's likely you'll come across some things that are tough to hear, truths you'd rather not face and facts you'd sooner ignore. You can do that but it won't work as well. So it may take a while before you can let down some of your guard and really let it in. Take it at your own pace. Get some support with it if you want to. Keep returning to this book, and eventually you'll be able to own it in a way that enables you to break through the barriers and access the power you already possess to take control. Then, things will change. Not just for a while but in real, lasting ways. Not because you read a book but because you changed the way you think about food.

GILLIAN'S STORY

My own progress with food has been gradual over a number of years, not at all dramatic but none the less valuable. I certainly eat a good deal less than I used to and the quality of what I eat has improved beyond recognition. I've made these changes in exactly the ways I describe in this book. I've certainly got the potential to be indulgent with food. I enjoy my food very much, but I also really enjoy being able to eat less.

For me, a healthy relationship with food is about eating things I need as much as it's about not eating things I don't need. I know it's not like this for everybody, but it's very easy for me to avoid eating fruit.

I write not only from my own experience but also as the result of all I've learned over twelve years of running seminars on dealing with overeating. People come to the seminars and we talk these things through. This book contains many of the experiences, the questions and the answers that have come out of this process.

Every time I lead a seminar I meet a new group and I learn more about what people need to understand so that eating less can become a natural part of their life. There's always a wide range of difficulties because everybody's different, but there are also themes I notice over and over again. I know they will help you because they have helped so many others in my seminars. Also, much of this approach is supported by scientific research, and that gives me a huge amount of confidence in the material in this book.

Some of my clients have contributed their comments at the ends of the chapters that follow. It may help you to see these ideas expressed in other people's words.

CHAPTER ONE

AM I CHOOSING?

Whenever you try to control what you eat, what kinds of things do you say to yourself? Do you think anything like this?

'I mustn't eat between meals.'
'I've got to stop eating all this bread.'
'I can't eat anything with sugar.'
'I'm not allowed to eat wheat.'
'Don't you dare eat any more of those.'

This style of thinking is very, very common so I wouldn't be at all surprised if these thoughts or something like them go through your head whenever you try to control your eating. Sometimes they flash by very quickly, so it takes some attention to catch them and realise that this is how you try to limit what you eat. Some people, though, gave up any attempt to control themselves so long ago they've banished these thoughts completely and just go ahead and eat anything they want. If this is so for you, see if you can become more aware of your thoughts. It might be that you could spot this style of thinking *after* you've been overeating:

'I've got to stop eating so much.'
'I shouldn't eat so much junk food/fried food/chocolate.'
'I won't allow myself chocolate for the rest of the week.'
'I must start that diet tomorrow.'
'I can't go on like this.'

Most people try to control their eating by thinking in terms of prohibition: commands, restrictions and threats. They think like an authority figure, a stern parent inside their own heads, shouting out orders. The harder they try, the more urgently this voice shouts at them, judges them and tries to bully them into submission.

This is what most people think of as willpower. It's no wonder they usually say they don't have any! I know I wouldn't want any of that. It sounds like a nightmare to me. In fact, it isn't willpower. It's the opposite of willpower and that's why it doesn't work. And it doesn't work, does it? If it did, you'd be out there obeying the orders, always being 'good', following the rules, never overeating or eating anything that's bad for you. The reality is more likely to be that the more you try to restrict yourself, the more you rebel and eat even more.

You might be one of those people who can go along with the rules for a while, perhaps when you're on a diet. You think, 'I am allowed to eat these things' (whatever's on the diet) and 'I'm not allowed to eat those things' (maybe just a few but not a lot of those things because they aren't on the diet). It works for a while but you know from experience that it doesn't last. At some point it all falls apart. Rebellious, out of control overeating kicks in again, you're eating even more than when you first started, and you keep putting off returning to the diet because it feels so restrictive. You think, 'I'll do that diet again one day, but not today. I'm too busy to think about it right now'. And so you go on, wishing you had some willpower with food.

The problem, you see, is created by thinking in terms of following rules and restrictions. Thinking this way creates a devastating attitude, which undermines your best intentions. This is the sense of deprivation, which will always destroy your attempts to control what you eat.

Feelings of deprivation are an adult version of the temper tantrum a child throws when they want something and are being prevented from getting it. This temper tantrum means you're going to be upset until you get what you want. You might think you don't go as far as throwing tantrums over food, but see if you don't throw a sophisticated, ever so subtle, adult version. An adult version which is just as deadly as the tantrums you see in the supermarkets from the kids with their exasperated mothers.

These deprivation tantrums can be so fleeting they're gone in a second. It can be the briefest glimpse of martyrdom, just at the thought of not eating this particular item you fancy. This feeling is so negative, it need do no more than threaten to appear. This threat is the fear that if you don't eat this thing *now* you're really going to regret it. If you deny yourself this thing, you aren't going to stop thinking about it, you'll eat something else that's even worse to compensate yourself, and when you do get you hands on some you'll eat ten times as many. You've got yourself over a barrel. You're damned if you do - but you're even more damned if you don't.

This is the nightmare so many people live with. They want to eat less, and especially less of certain things, but when they are attracted to these foods their willpower is nowhere to be found. It's been wiped out by the feeling of deprivation, even by the threat of it. And for those people who do manage to struggle through a few weeks or months of 'denying themselves', they can feel stressed, depressed and obsessed with food.

Eliminate this sense of deprivation and you get to access your willpower. You get to eat less in a way that can bring you joy and a sense of achievement instead of resentment, misery and sooner or later rebellious overeating again.

I realise you may just need to take my word for it at this point because you don't have your own experience to test this out yet, but what I want to explain to you in this chapter is that all this difficulty is created by a state of mind. The sense that eating less means you are 'denying yourself' is simply an attitude, a way of thinking. All that difficulty and negativity is created when you deny your freedom of choice, and you do that by thinking in terms of commands, threats, rules, restrictions and prohibition. Check out the sentences at the beginning of this chapter and see if any of them don't ever flip through your head. They leave you feeling like you're being bullied. Like you've been locked into a prison, forced to eat rabbit food and there's no way out.

Loss of freedom can be one of the most devastating things that can ever happen to a human being. This is true of any freedom that's rightfully yours: freedom of speech, for example, the right to vote and the right to worship. These and many more are all freedoms most of us take for granted but would object strongly if they were ever taken away. We also have every right to eat whatever is ours to eat – and that's the freedom you deny when you think in terms of 'can't', 'have to' and 'must'.

This is why it's the opposite of willpower. Willpower is the power of your will, and your will is free. When you deny free choice, you deny your free will. Then, you can't possibly use the power of your will, which is why you don't feel in control.

The solution is contained in the power of choice. When you choose, you access your will. In order to genuinely choose you need to know you've got choices: that you're completely free to eat anything and everything you might want. Everything changes when you get this and everything falls in place behind that. You don't feel deprived, you don't need or want to do any rebellious overeating and you find you have a far greater sense of control.

It's very straightforward and it turns everything on its head. Free choice. The rule is there are no rules. All you need to do is get used to thinking in this different way. It's really that simple. What's not so simple is putting this into action, because it takes some repetition to get it to sink in and become a reality for you.

As well as repetition, it may also take facing up to a fear which can block your path. This fear is that if you really let yourself believe you're completely free to eat anything – you will! That's why you deny choice in the first place, because you hope that if you give yourself a rule to follow you might obey it. It can take time to overcome this fear, to throw out the rules and let in a genuine sense of freedom around food. It will help a lot to fully own the choices you make by choosing the complete picture: the way you expect to feel after overeating, as well as the food.

Are you thinking you've heard all this before? I've often come across advice about making sure you don't deprive yourself of anything, so it's possible this is sounding a bit familiar. The advice I'm talking about is usually 'to eat whatever you want but in moderation', and the idea is that then you won't feel deprived. That's not what I'm saying here – and it's very important to understand the difference.

Perhaps you are already aware of the flaw in the standard advice. Setting out 'to eat what you want but in moderation' is all very well unless eating in moderation leaves you feeling deprived! After all, it is the immoderate amount you eat that you're trying to control in the first place, isn't it? The problem is that for many people eating enough to never feel deprived means overeating, and especially it means overeating things that are aren't good for your health.

Most people think being free to overeat means overeating. In other words, the thought, 'I'm free to eat that' is the same as, 'I'm going to go ahead and eat that.' Most people assert their freedom of choice about food by overeating. So whenever they try to eat less (by dieting or 'healthy eating') they deny choice. And this results in feelings of deprivation, denial and then a rebellious return to overeating.

What I'm suggesting is something else completely: that the difference between feeling deprived or not is in whether or not you genuinely believe you are choosing. You feel deprived when you forget you are the one who is choosing, and it's as if you've got the bad end of the deal. The difference is in your attitude; it has *very little to do with what and how much you are eating*. It's entirely possible not to eat for long periods of time and not feel deprived. It's entirely possible to feel tempted by food but not eat it and still not feel at all deprived. The reason is because you're remembering that it's your own free choice.

This of course takes some effort on your part. This isn't an instant, magic fix, but even starting to work with this will produce some results, and hopefully this will encourage you enough to want to continue. For most people, though, it does take a while to become real and more than just an interesting idea you read about in a book.

Consider this, though. It might be that this is the only way you can ever develop control over your eating. This might be it! Perhaps there never will be a pill you can take, a magic formula or a saviour who will come along and sort out this problem for you. It could be that you either continue to think in ways which make this problem worse, however gradually, over the years of your life. Or, you start to make changes, however gradually, that lead to you living your life more as you want to: in control of what you eat, calmer, healthier and enjoying a stronger sense of self-esteem that enhances everything you do.

The key is for you to experience what a difference it makes in your relationship with food when you genuinely choose. And you can only genuinely choose when you acknowledge your freedom to eat anything and everything you can get your hands on. When you connect with that freedom of choice, that experience will be of great significance to you because it will put everything into a different context.

It works especially well if you have good reasons for the choices you are making. In other words, you know what is motivating you, what is at stake. If you are clear about your motivation, you can make choices that you won't regret later on. That's what we'll look at in our next chapter.

WHAT YOU CAN DO

▸ Remind yourself you have a choice whenever you think about eating. Tell yourself, 'I can eat this' or 'this is my choice' whenever you eat *anything*.

It's especially important to do this if you are eating in a compulsive way and feeling out of control. This when you are most likely to revert to prohibitive thinking, so it's crucial to counteract this and reconnect with a genuine sense of choice. This means recognising that you can go on bingeing, that you can overeat all your life and that you never have to stop. You've got these choices – whether you want them or not. Then, and only then, you can freely choose how you really want to live.

▸ Whenever you're in a restaurant or food shop, let yourself know that you can eat anything you want and as much as you want. And you can return the next day and eat even more. Then, choose what really works for you, remembering the outcome of your different choices.

▸ Remind yourself of the outcome of the choices you are making. For example, 'I'm choosing to eat this tub of ice cream and to feel nauseous and guilty afterwards'. You are free to eat anything and everything; different choices, though, produce different results.

▸ If you feel deprived whenever you don't eat something you fancy, it's because you haven't yet created a genuine sense of choice for yourself. You might be paying lip service to the idea, you might understand the theory of it, but you don't yet feel it and experience it as a reality. That's OK! This is where many people start. The challenge for you is to continue to reinforce this theme of choice, so that eventually it becomes real and part of the way you always think about food.

▸ If you detect a rebellious quality to your eating, the same thing applies. Rebellion is only possible when there's a rule or restriction in place. Nobody can rebel if they have complete freedom, so remove the restrictions in the way you think and the rebelliousness disappears.

▸ Discussing these ideas as little as possible with the people in your life will give you a better sense of your own choices. If someone makes a comment about what you're eating or not eating, just refuse to get involved in a conversation about it and concentrate on your own process in private. It's your own thinking you want to concentrate on. No matter what anybody else says, it's your own thinking that makes the difference.

▸ When you ask yourself: 'Am I choosing?' see if you feel and believe that you are always totally free to overeat, especially when you're not eating something that's tempting you.

MIRIAM'S STORY

I'm a mother of three, a wife and a manager of a software company. I did Gillian's seminar about a year ago and my eating has transformed, I would say. I do slide occasionally but I have many very good weeks now.

I think the major thing that still grabs me is this thing about choice. I simply refused to put myself back in prison by stopping dieting. But, I'm choosing to eat a lot fewer biscuits, for example. I know now that it's my free choice, that I can do it if I want to but I don't have to. I used to eat so much simply because I thought I wouldn't be able to later on, so I wanted to get as much in while I still could. It was like I was always on the verge of a famine.

I was completely caught up in the trap of repeatedly dieting and bingeing, dieting and bingeing, for several years. I would go to various kinds of slimming groups and find myself eating frantically as soon as I had been weighed. I used to have this thing about Sundays, because I would always start my diet again on Monday and I used to eat all day Sunday. Today, it's Sunday and I'm just delighted about the way I have eaten. I was thinking earlier I'd have some toast, and I thought no, I'll wait for supper. It seems so normal to think that way now and yet it was never like that before. There was always so much struggle.

It's had an effect on other things in my life as well. I'm more conscious when I say I've 'got to' do something. I didn't get it at first, but I now realise the things I take on are my choice, so it comes back to me when I think 'oh no, I've got to do all this.' I remember that it's my choice and then it isn't a burden. In general I like being busy but often it gets too much.

The benefit to me is definitely in terms of self-esteem and it's a huge relief not to be on that diet bandwagon. I really enjoy eating and I really enjoy feeling in control. I feel liberated. I'm going to make a cabbage salad this evening. I positively enjoy that sort of thing now.

CHAPTER TWO

WHY DOES IT MATTER?

Why are you reading a book about beating overeating? Most people would be very clear about their answer: 'Because I want to lose weight more than anything in the world.' Everywhere you look – at your friends, at TV, in magazines – people are talking about wanting to lose weight. They say things like:

'I'm tired of living in this fat body.'
'I look in the mirror and I'm depressed for the rest of the day.'
'If only I was thinner my life would be so much better.'
'I'd love to walk into a room and not feel self-conscious because of my size.'
'I've struggled with my weight all my life.'
'If I could either win the lottery or be thin, I'd rather be thin.'

Of course there's no shortage of solutions offered to help you lose weight. Diets, low-fat foods and slimming clubs all promise to take inches off your thighs and fat off your backside. The problem is *weight* and the solution is *to lose it*.

It seems so simple and yet, as we all know, very few people are actually succeeding. Currently, about one in four adults in Great Britain are obese. Not just a bit flabby. Obese, which is roughly 40 pounds overweight. The majority of our population, both men and women, weigh more than is good for their health. It's just as bad across most of Europe and even worse in America. The pressure to be slim comes from every angle, yet we, together with most of the western industrialised nations, are getting heavier and heavier. That should be our first clue that something is very wrong. Maybe motivation to lose weight isn't as straight-forward as it seems.

Why don't we try thinking about all this in a completely different way? I'm going to suggest one change in attitude by first of all making an analogy.

Let's imagine that one day you walk into your kitchen and see to your horror that your kitchen floor is flooded with water, three or four inches deep. Now that's a problem for you, isn't it? You panic, grab a mop and bucket and try to get rid of the water, thinking, 'Oh dear, oh dear, all this dreadful water all over the place, how can I make it go away, it's so horrible and wet, and there's so much of it.' And you mop and mop and mop.

In the middle of all this, someone walks in and points out to you that over at the sink the tap is running, the sink is blocked and the water keeps pouring out. You can see what they're saying, but you don't care very much about the tap and the sink. What you really care about is your floor, so that's what you concentrate on, mopping up the floor and fretting about the water. You have some people coming round and you're afraid they'll see the floor and all the dreadful water. You can hide the tap and the sink behind a screen and they'll never know it's there, but they'll be disgusted if all that water is there on the floor. If only you could get the water cleaned up.

You worry about the water for a long time. Whenever you talk about this problem with your friends, you talk about the water on the floor. Whenever your friends talk to you about it, they ask about the water, how deep it is and how you are doing with the mopping. Weeks go by. Then months. Then years. The water is still there, getting deeper and deeper, and you get more and more worried about it as time goes on.

This story illustrates what happens when you focus on the effect of a problem, the water on the floor, instead of its cause, the running tap. The story may seem rather unrealistic, but the chances are that you too have spent most of your time wanting to change the *effect* of your problem instead of the *cause*.

You've probably tried to 'mop up' your excess weight by dieting. You've set goals for yourself to lose weight, such as, 'I want to lose a dress size before my summer holidays.' And you've seen success or failure by how much weight you lost or gained. In the analogy, you are chiefly concerned with the floor, trying to get it dry and gauging success by how dry or wet it is. You know there's a tap running somewhere, but it's not nearly as important, is it?

Clearly there's something here that we all know: in general, dealing directly with the cause of any problem is going to work much better than trying to take care of the effects. In the analogy, if you dealt with the cause by getting the tap and the sink to do the work they were designed for, in time the water would evaporate and it will be fairly easy to keep dry. In the same way, when you eat the food that your body was designed for, in time, the weight evaporates and the weight loss is fairly easy to maintain.

Do you think you've been trying to do this already? Maybe, but it's also likely that what really matters to you has been your weight. Glance back to the beginning of the chapter and see if you don't identify with those first statements. That's what's motivating you, isn't it? Weight loss. Wanting to lose weight is very likely the main reason you're reading this book. No matter how much you want it, it's still a weak motivation because it keeps you locked into the effect of the problem. You're still trying to mop up the water. Endlessly. This is one of the reasons so few people are succeeding, even though they want it so much.

Now when you think about it, dealing with the cause of a

problem is the obvious answer, so, you might ask, why doesn't everybody just figure this out for themselves? There are a number of reasons for this, but one common factor is low self-esteem. Low self-esteem can keep you locked into seeing your problem entirely in terms of the size and the shape of your body. Low self-esteem means that making the switch from effect to cause, far from being obvious and simple, is in fact a challenge. This really is a big key to understanding how to motivate yourself in a much more powerful way, so let's understand it a bit.

Low self-esteem means that being slimmer is all that matters. Very crudely put, it's like thinking something like this: 'I don't think very much of myself, but if I looked really good or at least better than I do now, I might convince someone that I'm OK and maybe worth having around.'

This creates a dreadful relationship with food. An extreme example is someone who eats a chocolate bar for lunch, a packet of crisps for dinner and wouldn't dream of sitting down to a real meal because it has too many calories in it. Such a person places so little value on herself or himself they don't regard their health as worth supporting.

That's extreme, but I wouldn't be surprised if you too make many decisions about what you eat based on what you look like rather than your nutritional needs – whether you are overeating or not. This way of thinking about food is, at least in large part, based on the judgement of others. It reinforces the low self-esteem, which in turn reinforces this way of thinking.

You might think, as many do, that if only you lost weight, your self-esteem would improve because you'd feel so proud of the way you looked. But it doesn't quite work that way, as many people who have achieved their ideal weight know too well. I often hear people say they felt as miserable when they were skinny as when they were fat. Often that surprised them because they thought that 'looking good' would solve everything.

Sometimes, though, you hear people say, 'Yes, losing weight is wonderful but it's not the most important thing, because I really enjoy so much about the way I'm living now.' That's closer to what I'm getting to, and I want to suggest that the people who think like this tend to be more successful in the long term. What makes the difference is they found ways to motivate themselves to eat less that aren't *exclusively* about how much they weigh and what they look like.

Don't get me wrong; there's absolutely nothing wrong with losing weight – assuming of course that you are overweight to start with. It's when you can put that to one side and discover other reasons to take control of your overeating that things really start to change. You lose weight too, but it's a side effect rather than the focus of everything.

There are a number of reasons why weight loss doesn't work as your main reason to eat less. First of all, it gives you delayed feedback. For example, if you didn't binge on junk food one evening, you may wake up the next morning feeling a bit more alert and energised. That's far more rapid feedback for you, letting you know that you're on the right track, than the bit of weight you *might* have lost as a result of the control you took the previous evening. It's also much more clearly connected to that particular choice you made about not overeating. It's not so easy to say that any one binge will end up as any one particular bulge of fat on your hips!

Most important of all, though, is that motivating yourself to lose weight only works until your weight is lost. When you've lost weight, there's no longer any good reason not to binge in the evenings – and so you do! So, pay attention to all the other things that are at stake, such as feeling in control, having more energy, no stomach aches, sleeping better, clearer thinking or more positive mood.

It's these sorts of things that can motivate you – if you can notice and pay attention to them – even before you've lost very much weight. And this is especially important if you have a lot of weight to lose. As you may know, it's a slow process, and losing two pounds after a week, although a brilliant result, can seem a drop in the ocean. So, look for anything else that you might be enjoying because you've been eating less. Make a point of remembering these things, as they will continue to provide you with motivation, greatly reducing the likelihood that you will yo-yo back up again.

This is a completely different way to motivate yourself and it's a way that's much more effective, especially over the course of a lifetime. It's about eating in a way that supports and enhances your emotional and your physical well-being. It's about correcting the balance from a situation where losing weight is everything to just having it be a factor, a bonus. It's fine to have both kinds of motivation. Most of us do. We will always want to look as good as we can and there's nothing wrong with that. What makes the difference is having both kinds of motivation in a good balance.

When you draw the focus of your attention away from trying to lose weight and towards looking after your health, you immediately start to boost your self-esteem. This is because you are affirming that you value yourself enough to give your body what's best for it. You motivate yourself towards having a healthy relationship with food rather than looking a certain way. You can have both. You can have the best of health and look great too, but if you prioritise genuine health and self-esteem you will connect with a considerably more powerful and enduring source of motivation. Then, the weight loss pretty much takes care of itself.

WHAT YOU CAN DO

▸ Identify any motivation that's anything other than weight loss. It's not that losing weight is a bad thing; it's just that we need to correct an imbalance because weight loss – what other people can see and judge us by – has become much too important in most people's minds. Is there anything you like about eating less, besides losing weight? Make the effort to notice how your life is better when you eat in healthier ways. Do you have more energy to get through your day, so that you enjoy your evenings more? Fewer headaches? Better digestion? Do you notice that your self-esteem is higher? Is it simply that you enjoy being in control of your eating?

It will help you to write these things down so you can remember them later on. Write as much as you can, with your own personal details. And leave out anything to do with your size, shape and weight. It might take a bit of thinking about this before you can come up with complete answers, but every time you do you'll be developing much more effective and enduring motivation.

▸ Take note of any signs of poor (or just not-so-great) health you may have. You could think of them as messages sent from your body asking you to make changes in what and how much you eat. Many people these days are eating in ways that upset various processes in the body, and then take medication to 'correct' that upset, instead of changing what they eat.

▸ If appearance is your main motivation, find ways to play it down so that you can bring it into a more sustainable perspective. Instead of setting weight loss targets, aim to eat in a way that best supports your physical and emotional well-being. Whenever you think you'd like to weigh yourself, simply remind yourself of those other benefits.

This probably won't come naturally at first, it usually takes deliberate effort. Discuss your weight as little as possible, whether you've lost some or not. Refuse to join conversations about dieting and weight. If someone says something like, 'You look good – have you lost weight?' say as little about it as you can. Change the subject if you possibly can.

▸ Be especially careful any time you lose weight. Have you ever lost weight and immediately started eating more? It's very common. Losing weight gets you attached to the effect again, taking you off track with the cause. This is one place you can see just how counterproductive weight loss is as your primary motivation. Especially at first, keep as quiet as you can about any lost weight, concealing it under baggy clothes and not mentioning it to anyone. Sounds crazy, doesn't it? But it works.

It's best to think of weight loss as a kind of anti-motivation that gets in the way of your more effective motivation, which is genuine health and self-esteem. It can make a big difference because then you move from motivation that reinforces lower self-esteem to motivation that reinforces higher self-esteem. And it's higher self-esteem that will continue to work for you in the longer term.

▸ If you find it extremely difficult to make this shift in your motivation, perhaps in part because you don't see any health benefits even when you do eat healthier food, it may well be because you are fairly young – in your teens or twenties perhaps. The change in the priorities of your motivation that I'm describing here becomes more relevant as you get older, when the body starts to become less efficient.

▸ If you want to lose weight for health reasons, don't assume that this chapter has no relevance for you. Many people are aware of the health risks of their excess weight and still have strong emotional attachment bound up in their appearance.

▸ Find ways to improve the quality of your meals. Are you one of those people who have settled for a mediocre way of eating, telling yourself it's healthy when in fact it could be quite a bit better? Are you still counting calories? Start to think in terms of eating for nutritional needs. Counting calories means you are focused on weight loss. Caring more about the nutritional content of your meals means you are building your health and self-esteem. More about this later on.

▸ Make a note of everything you eat for a few days. If you haven't ever done this before, it can be a brave and powerful step. Some overeaters see their problem in terms of weight because they are unaware of just how much they eat. Break through this, if you are ready, by writing it all down as you go. When you review your notes later on, you may be in for a surprise. Research has shown that overweight people tend to underestimate the amount they eat by as much as 800 calories a day, and honestly don't know they're doing it.

▸ When you ask yourself: 'Why does it matter?' find reasons that don't depend on losing weight. It's important to use your own experiences as much as you can. The best motivation of all could be to slow down the process of aging, to stay younger and healthier for longer in your life. You strengthen your self-esteem in the present time when you motivate yourself this way. Weight loss will follow – and it is much more likely to last.

MARTHA'S STORY

Self-esteem is what clicked for me. I've been through a lot of traumas recently and I've been very low and this has been a way forward for me. At the moment I'm clearing all the junk out of my house, throwing it all out, and that's all been part of it. So it's been a whole life change.

I know it's not about weight but I've lost 14 pounds so far. I'm not completely happy with my eating but I'm not bingeing any more so that's nice. I'd like to find better ways to cook vegetables and plan my menus ahead of time and I'm not doing that yet. I'm making things up as I go along and too often that degenerates into lots of ready-made meals and sandwiches. So that's one of the things I still want to change.

The changes have been gradual and sensible and it's definitely lasting. I don't fear that suddenly I'm going to start bingeing again, day after day, like I used to. I may overeat once but it's not the end of the world. I know it won't mean going down that slippery slope into that scary out of control stuff. Overeating is just not OK with me. This new perspective on things has helped me sharpen up my eating so much. It's about honouring myself and the impact that has on everything and every aspect of your life. I feel so much better now, when I think about all of it I just feel good.

I joined a gym and started exercising but I found it so boring I didn't keep it up. Now I take the dog for a walk every day. A long walk, for about an hour, and I prefer that. I get up in the morning and take the dog out before I go to work. Sometimes in the evenings I can walk for hours.

I'm thinking about choices a lot more and when I get stuck with something in my life I'm much more likely to think, 'Do I really have to do this?' And often I don't. This doesn't mean I'm doing less. I'm feeling even more productive these days, and creative and on top of things in general. I'm doing things because I want to do them, not because I have to.

CHAPTER THREE

HOW AM I RESPONDING TO TEMPTATION?

You might call it an impulse or an urge. You might call it a snack attack. You fancy something. You want to eat when you know you're not hungry. You want to go on eating when you've just finished a meal. It's happening in all those moments when you wish you had some control. Many people call it a craving. For reasons we'll look at in a moment, it's what I call an 'addictive desire to eat'.

The chances are you think of your desire to overeat as an enemy because it seems to make you eat despite your very best intentions. It seems to overpower you, so the only way you can think of to escape its power is to avoid it. So, if being bored brings it on you make sure you're always busy. If eating out holds the most temptation for you, you stop going to restaurants. If you tend to overeat in front of the TV, you turn it off and find other ways to fill your evenings.

Eventually, though, your addictive desire returns. You try to satisfy it with a glass of water or a few carrot sticks, but what you really want is something much more sugary and creamy or oily and salty. Or you find you really can stop eating all the rubbish food but overeat healthy food compulsively. So you continue to satisfy your addictive desire to eat, and wonder how you will ever be able to stop eating so much.

Most people know that running away from a problem does nothing to solve it. Yet this is the very strategy they try to use to control their overeating. At first it might seem to work, but only up to a point, and the reason it stops working is simply that it's impossible to avoid temptation forever. Food is there in your life every day, almost everywhere you go, and a lot of it will tempt you – as if you didn't know that already!

So let's look at an alternative, because there really is another way of approaching this, a way that's completely different to anything you've ever tried before. It's such an unconventional solution, though; this way may at first seem strange, impossible and even outrageous. It may take a while before you can really grasp it – but when you do you'll find it works like a charm.

What I'm going to suggest is that you look at this addictive desire to eat and think of it as your friend instead of your enemy.

Well, I did say outrageous, didn't I? Bear with me, just continue to read and see if there aren't some things here that give you a glimpse that this may be, not only possible, but very effective.

Just consider that if you did make friends with your desire to overeat, you wouldn't fear it and you wouldn't need to run away from it. But most of all, you wouldn't have to satisfy it. You'd feel genuinely tempted from time to time and you'd feel absolutely fine about that. Maybe sometimes you'd eat in response to that temptation, *but you wouldn't have to*. In this way you'd be able to keep yourself from eating so much, not because you'd avoided temptation but because you'd learned to live with it, happily and easily.

There are good reasons why I don't call it a craving. A craving is often regarded as an intense and miserable experience, and you know from Chapter 1 that this is created by the state of deprivation. Cravings belong to the temper tantrum of the deprived child who wants something they can't have. When you create a feeling of free choice for yourself – and this will need to be recreated from time to time as you remind yourself of your choices – those more intense, unacceptable cravings simply evaporate.

Not only that, but the word 'craving' doesn't always describe your experience of desire. An addictive desire to eat can be strong and persistent at times, especially when you're first working with this approach, but it can also be extremely subtle.

Sometimes it's no more than a simple thought, so brief it's almost unnoticeable. It can simply be, 'Oh yes, I'd like some of that.' This is not what we usually think of as craving, so I use the term 'addictive desire to eat' to include both the stronger feelings and the fleeting thoughts.

It makes a huge difference to be able to identify even those brief thoughts of desire because a great deal of overeating gets done in a fairly unconscious way. You may not be aware you are feeding an addictive desire, and maybe not too aware of what and how much you're eating either. It's impossible to control something you aren't aware of, so noticing and naming your desire to eat is a crucial first step. If you just think in terms of 'craving' you'll miss a lot of it.

Becoming aware of addictive desire is, of course, just the first step. It's a hugely significant step, but even when you've named it you still want to overeat in some way. You need to handle this experience so that you've got the option not to satisfy your desire, or at least not to satisfy it quite so much, quite so often. This is where we get back to that idea of making the desire your friend.

As with any friendship, understanding goes a long way towards making friends. Essentially, an addictive desire to eat is an expectation of eating, and the best way to understand it is as a memory. It's the memory you have of overeating in the past. It's easy to check this out in your own experience. If you have a snack every time you walk into your kitchen, then walking into your kitchen will make you want a snack. If you eat every time you feel upset, then every time you feel upset you'll want to eat something. If you buy a chocolate bar every time you pay for petrol when you fill your car, you will inevitably desire your 'treat' every time you're there.

This is called the 'conditioned response' and was first described by the scientist Ivan Pavlov, while investigating how salivation works. He rang a bell every time he fed his dogs and then observed that the dogs salivated any time they heard the bell, thinking food was on its way. In the same way, we train ourselves to associate food with all kinds of cues in our lives. And, as with the dogs, the response can be physical; not only salivation but also what feels like stomach hunger and genuine need.

This is why your addictive desire to eat can at times be felt as sensations in your body. Body and mind are powerfully connected, in communication all the time, so thoughts often show up as physical feelings. For example, the thought, 'Oh my god I've locked my keys in the car!' can produce an undeniable sinking feeling the stomach. In the same way, the thought of wanting to eat something may show up as a sensation of hungry emptiness.

Well, maybe it is hunger, I hear you say. Not if you've just finished a meal it isn't. That's your addictive desire to eat, simply you thinking you want more because that's what you've done in the past. It's your addictive desire that wants to be satisfied. This is why you can sometimes eat and eat and eat and eat and eat and never satisfy this addictive, excess appetite.

The addictive desire isn't just any ordinary memory, though; it's a memory of something that was pleasurable and satisfying. It's produced by our survival system, which rewards us (with so-called 'feel-good' brain chemicals such as serotonin and dopamine) for behaviours that are supposed to be life-enhancing. Food that contains sugar, wheat, fats and/or salt activates these rewards much more powerfully, which is what makes them more addictive.

This makes them more compelling and why you experience a *desire* for them, rather than an impartial memory of having eaten them in the past. Even when you eat a healthy meal you inevitably experience reward (pleasure and satisfaction) and that's why eating anything at all can awaken a desire for more.

Understanding that your addictive desire is an inevitable memory helps you to accept that it will be a part of your life. It doesn't mean you are mad, bad or greedy. It doesn't mean you're doing anything wrong and that you need to do something – go into therapy or find exactly the right diet – to make it go away. It simply means you have eaten in an addictive way in this circum- stance in the past and you have a memory of that. You've got choices, but one choice you don't have is to erase your memory.

You either reinforce this memory by overeating once again, or start to make a change by leaving it unsatisfied. If you leave the addictive desire unsatisfied, you get to be in control of your overeating – and in time it fades.

You may be thinking that it's going to be tough to make friends with something that seems to overwhelm and control you. You may know that the addictive desire can put you into a kind of trance, when you want to eat and all other thoughts disappear from your mind. You forget why you wanted to stop eating so much. You forget how good you feel when you eat more wisely. You get mesmerised, and all you can think about is food.

When, in the past, you avoided temptation and any feeling of desire, you never learned how to work through this trance state, so you're always going to be its victim when it's there. Far more powerful is to develop the skill of talking yourself through it, by turning around to face it and deal with it. At first, though, even when you do face it, you may still fight it and struggle with it simply because you hate it and really you just wish it would go away. This actually makes things worse because the more you fight something like this the more it is going to fight back.

You stop fighting your addictive desire by accepting it, so that it simply flows through you without any opposition. You let yourself relax into the feeling and let the addictive desire to eat be there. This doesn't necessarily mean that you're enjoying yourself; it is, after all, an uncomfortable sensation. It simply means you are willing to feel uncomfortable for a while. You learn how to think yourself out of and break the trance by paying attention to it and choosing to let yourself experience it.

Accepting it makes things a lot easier. It's best to accept it unconditionally, but mostly you'll find that if you really are choosing to accept it, it doesn't hang around for nearly as long. There may be a few days, especially at first, when it's there a lot, but this diminishes over time. It's a paradox: the more you genuinely accept it, the more it fades.

Accept it by thinking of this uncomfortable, unsatisfied desire as the price you pay for the control over food that you want. If someone offered you a fortune to accept feeling your addictive desire just once, I wouldn't be surprised if you'd do it. So, it's just a matter of figuring out for yourself whether what you're really going to get is worth it to you. What you get isn't a fortune in money, but the good fortune of the quality of your life and your health when you are eating less. That is exactly how you take control of overeating, by re-evaluating your priorities. You can only do that – properly – while you are feeling your unsatisfied addictive desire.

It's impossible to learn how to swim without being in some water. It's impossible to learn how to drive without getting into a car. In the same way, you will not learn how to take control of your overeating until you let yourself experience your addictive desire to eat and talk yourself through it.

I find this concept is often quite difficult for people to really understand, but makes the biggest difference when they do. Often people will make all kinds of plans about how they are going to eat more sensibly, but they forget about addictive desire. Then, when temptation strikes, their plans are forgotten and they are left wondering why they didn't follow through. It's fine to want to make changes, to have an intention, for example, to eat less bread. Just remember that this choice doesn't actually get made until you're thinking about fixing your mid-morning toast snack. It's how you deal with that experience of addictive desire that makes the difference.

Of course it's crucial to know you have got free choice about what you do, but often people think in terms of making a choice to eat or not to eat something. So they think, 'Shall I eat the toast or not?' That is the result, but it's not the best way to think about it. It's much better to put powerful words to the process because by describing it correctly you create an entirely new attitude towards eating.

The best way is to think, 'Right now, have an addictive desire to eat.' Even if that's as far as you go, that will be something, but it's good not to stop there. Then, you can say, 'I could go ahead and eat some toast or I could just let myself feel this addictive desire. Yes, it feels uncomfortable but I'd rather have this feeling than spend the rest of my life overeating. It's worth it to me because it means I'll feel more in control, I'll enjoy my lunch more and feel more proud of myself.'

The more you make your choices in this way, the easier it will become and the more natural it will seem. You make the addictive desire your friend because when you accept it as part of your life you get to break free from overeating and all that goes with it. You let it live with you because by doing so, as a direct result, you can control what and how much you eat. You accept it because it will change your life. It could even save your life.

This is about facing the difficulty of making a genuine, lasting change in your relationship with food. This is about dealing with this problem in everyday, practical experience. You choose, and the way you choose is either to satisfy your addictive desire or to accept it by being willing to feel it by leaving it unsatisfied. Fundamentally, those are the choices that are open to you.

Of course you aren't going to stop eating entirely, so one of the challenges you face is to know the difference between an addictive desire and a genuine need to eat. Contrary to popular belief, we don't possess bodies that can naturally provide us with this information. Our bodies want to get us to eat as much as possible, whenever possible, and even one hundred years ago that wasn't much of a problem.

These days, there's so much food around, and especially so much manufactured, addictive food. Instead of trying to rely on bodies that are better suited to another era, we need to *think* ourselves out of this problem.

So that you can get better at identifying your addictive desire, let's look briefly at what it isn't.

NATURAL HUNGER is a sense of emptiness in your stomach, a natural signal from your body telling you it's time to eat. It will come and go, and although it's wise to eat something soon, you won't feel compelled to eat unless it's accompanied by addictive desire. In fact, you can feel perfectly happy, energised and alert when your body isn't being overworked by digesting food all the time.

It's fine to aim for natural hunger at meal times, but don't worry if you don't feel it. It can go missing when logic tells you it really should be there, and it could be that you realise how hungry you are only after you've started eating.

Not only is natural hunger unreliable, but waiting until you are hungry before you eat can be quite inconvenient when you need to fit in meal times with other people. The chances are that you'll have something to do so that it's not practical to eat later on, when you'll be running your errands, teaching a class or attending a meeting.

You may in the past have been advised to eat only when you feel naturally hungry. Some people get into difficulty with food simply because they continually fall short of this impossible goal. This is why it's best to simply consider when it would be appropriate to eat again. There will always be some guesswork here, but make your best guess about what you think would be *reasonable*, rather than *addictive*. The more you can identify and manage your addictive desire, the easier this will become.

ACID INDIGESTION can be painful, and many sufferers overeat simply to make it go away. Even the fear that you might get hungry later on is likely to cause you to overeat so that you won't feel the pain of an acid stomach. Antacid medications are not good for your health if you take them regularly, so it's much better to correct the problem directly.

Alcohol and caffeine contribute to over-acidity, but cigarette smoking is the biggest cause. As for food, nutritionists often recommend a balance of 20 per cent acid-forming foods (mostly meat, poultry, fish, eggs and cheese) with 80 per cent alkaline-forming foods (vegetables and fruits). Also helpful is to keep sugar and wheat to minimum, as they are common contributors to an overly acid body, and to take regular exercise and plenty of (alkaline) water. Acidity can lead to very serious health problems, so it's important to deal with this, quite apart from eliminating this cause of false hunger.

LOW BLOOD SUGAR comes from the rapid rise and fall of insulin and glucose in the bloodstream caused by overeating certain kinds of carbohydrates. This connection between carbohydrates and insulin and glucose release is rated by what is known as the glycemic load (or glycemic index).

Carbohydrates that trigger a strong response of insulin and glucose are said to have a high glycemic load. It's no coincidence that these are mostly foods which people tend to overeat and have difficulty controlling. They provide a drug-like 'fix' but, like most drugs, they let you down soon after. This let-down, the low blood sugar, is another cause of false hunger. Carbohydrates with a high glycemic load include: breakfast cereals, rice cakes, wheat bread and crackers, popcorn, most rice, pastry, cakes, croissants and most things containing refined sugar or glucose syrup.

Carbohydrates that cause insulin and glucose to be released more moderately are rated as having a 'low glycemic load.' They provide the body with sustained energy and mental alertness, and include vegetables, fruits, rye and oats.

If you often feel hungry, irritable or drowsy during the day, especially mid-morning, late afternoon or soon after eating, low blood sugar may be the reason. Here is an example, which has come up a few times in my seminars. Someone eats what they consider to be a substantial, healthy breakfast of commercial cereal or wheat toast but gets so hungry by mid-morning they have great difficulty waiting until lunch time before they eat again. Eating a larger breakfast doesn't make things any better. Eating low glycemic load carbohydrates for breakfast – oats, rye toast and fruit for example – makes all the difference.

If you experience these sudden and otherwise inexplicable drops of energy, think back to what you last ate and see if it included high glycemic load carbohydrates. Your brain needs a lot of glucose to function well, so you could feel sluggish mentally as well.

You can find your biggest breakthrough by understanding that your addictive desire to eat is not just something to be endured, but actually makes real change possible. If it's dealt with properly, this excess appetite will fade from your life. This is partly because you are no longer reinforcing it by overeating and partly because you are paying attention to this process. We look at how this happens in our next chapter.

WHAT YOU CAN DO

▸ Don't expect to be able to manage your addictive desire every time. Sometimes you won't even notice it and sometimes you might not be willing to accept it. This is a process, and you will be on a learning curve. Stay with it and you will get where you want to go.

▸ Notice your addictive desire to eat as often as you can, so that you develop the awareness you need to take control. It's only when you've named it that you can make a choice about it. If you aren't aware of it, it will run you.

▸ At first it may be difficult to identify, so try setting a time goal so that your addictive desire will stand out more clearly. Setting a time goal means you agree with yourself that you intend not to eat until a certain time. Do this during those times when you want to take control of snacking or grazing. Make sure you always remind yourself you have the option of eating, even before you get to your chosen time.

▸ Allow yourself to feel your addictive desire. This is where you take control. One place your addictive desire is sure to show up is at the end of a meal. Have a clear picture in your mind of what you intend to eat before you start. When you finish the amount you planned (assuming, of course, it's less than usual!) you will want to go on, and this is your addictive desire. You can practice managing this desire at the end of meals.

▸ Be willing to end your meals feeling unsatisfied. Sometimes you hear advice to 'eat until you're full' but this doesn't take the addictive desire into account. Most people want to continue eating after finishing a meal of a reasonable size. It's likely you won't feel satisfied until you've overeaten so much that you're physically and psychologically uncomfortable, much too full and maybe even feeling guilty and disappointed with yourself. Your way out of this nightmare is to allow yourself to feel unsatisfied when you end your meal.

▸ Notice when you have fallen into that trance-like state during a meal, when you are eating much too fast. It might not be possible to stop this immediately, but any time you become aware that you are 'shovelling it in', sit back in your chair, put your fork down, take a breath and then resume eating. In time you will get used to eating more slowly.

▸ There may be no need to abstain from your 'binge' or 'trigger' foods. Whenever you eat your favourite 'drug', be it sugar, chocolate, nuts, bread or whatever, your addictive desire for them may be awakened. It might be easier for you to cut them out completely, but abstinence can be unrealistic long term, and not at all necessary once you learn how to manage addictive desire. It's important to eat in a way you can continue to live with, to have some flexibility and variation.

▸ When your favourite, addictive foods are close at hand, you're likely to feel more of a desire for them. It might be better not to have some things in the house because they drive you crazy, so find what works best for you. At least be aware that by having certain things around you, your addictive desire for them may be more persistent. You might find it works better to accept your addictive desire for them when you're in the supermarket, and choose to leave them there on the shelves.

▸ Notice the difference between an enjoyment of food, which is both positive and appropriate, and the 'high' you get when you satisfy your addictive desire. It's important to enjoy what you eat, but some people eat so much highly addictive food – mostly sugar, wheat, salt and fats – they lose their taste for proper food such as vegetables. Junk food satisfies your addictive desire. Real food satisfies your nutritional needs. They are quite different experiences and it will help you a lot to learn how to tell them apart. This is especially important if you tend to justify overeating by thinking, 'I really enjoy my food – what's wrong with that?'

▸ Remind yourself why you are accepting this unsatisfied desire by thinking of what benefits you gain by not overeating. Look for reasons other than weight loss and find your own, selfish reasons. It may be energy or it may be a sense of freedom, control or accomplishment. Just have it be something for yourself, something that's a joy to you in your life. Then it will be easier for you to accept the uncomfortable feeling of unsatisfied desire – because the trade-off is a good one.

▸ An intense or persistent craving is a sure sign you're feeling deprived and it's vital you change your way of thinking so that it doesn't wear you down. If you're feeling deprived it's because you've forgotten that you've got complete freedom about what you do, or maybe that you're just paying lip service to the idea without really believing it. You might hold out until a good excuse comes along, but when you feel deprived you're likely to create a good excuse if one doesn't show up on its own.

▸ Don't be put off by the word 'addiction'. It refers to the food you eat that you don't actually need. Mostly, this food is enjoyable, available, common and thoroughly integrated into our lives. There is a biochemical side to addiction, but your biochemistry doesn't have the last word regarding what actions you will take. Certain kinds of food – especially sugar, wheat, salt and fat – have an effect on our biochemistry, and this is why they have a more addictive quality to them. In other words, it's easy to eat them far too much if you don't know how to deal with your addictive desire for them.

▸ Ask yourself: 'How am I responding to temptation?' and notice your addictive desire, and what you're doing about it. Feeding it unconsciously? Or paying attention to it and thinking it through? You could begin to notice and make choices to accept this desire to eat as the trade-off for the benefits which come from eating less. The more you do that, the less you will be overeating. And in time your addictive desire to eat will fade.

KAREN'S STORY

I had been obese for almost ten years and I had high blood pressure and a strong fear that I would become diabetic. I had talked about this with my doctor and she often warned me about my weight. I had dieted all my life and failed at it all my life. I felt really quite miserable about the whole thing. Nothing I did worked, but it wasn't for lack of trying.

I did a counselling course for years and went through endless hours of counselling in a determined effort to get to the bottom of my overeating. There were other issues too and the counselling helped a lot with some of them, but my eating was always the main problem and the one that felt impossible to change.

I always believed that if I could only find the root cause of my eating problem, find out what was behind it and heal that, then I would be able to stop overeating. This assumption, far from being challenged by the people running the course, was actively encouraged. For much of my life I carried around a strong sense that there was something wrong with me, something I could never discover and which my overeating continuously confirmed.

All that's changed now. When I did Gillian's seminar I kept waiting for the other shoe to drop, waiting for the cravings to return, but they never did. My addictive desire is a completely different thing, nothing like I used to feel when I was dieting, or I should say, trying to diet. I never before had made the connection between what I ate and the state of my health. Before, it was always about weight, about how I looked. Now eating healthy foods and not eating unhealthy ones makes tremendous sense. It's all so obvious to me now but you can get yourself into such amazing muddles about food and eating and weight.

The concept that remains with me the most is about the addictive side of eating because I now know what to do when I'm feeling 'hungry' which of course isn't feeling hungry at all. It doesn't happen nearly as much as it used to, it's changed. I'm realising there are periods of time when I have this addictive hunger, and that I don't have to satisfy it.

At the moment I'm doing a 28-day detox and I find it very interesting because I'm not eating wheat. I hadn't realised how very 'moorish' bread was, and that's something that's really come home to me. I'm eating rye bread on this detox so I'm still eating bread, but I'm not doing that continuous nibbling that I used to do with the regular bread.

CHAPTER FOUR

HOW TO GET A NEW BRAIN

Have you ever thought you'd need a new brain before you could control your overeating? I've heard people say this in my seminars. Well, guess what – you can get one! Not completely new (I expect there are a few bits you'd like to keep) but the part of your brain associated with wanting to eat so much can actually be physically altered! By you!

It might sound unbelievable but this is exactly what will happen when you follow the guidelines set out in this book. It's not really all that bizarre; in fact, it's a completely natural process that happens to us all. It just helps so much if you understand what it is you're doing so that you know why you are following a particular course of action. Then you can be more deliberate about it and therefore more effective. So this is what this chapter is about.

First of all, understand a very simple principle about how

your brain works: that the job of every cell in your brain is to communicate with other cells. Each cell does this by pulsing signals to the next brain cell which in turn signals to the next, setting off a chain reaction, one cell to the next, to the next, to the next, hundreds and thousands and millions of times across your brain. It's doing it right now!

There are billions and billions of brain cells, and each signal could travel in any direction. But they don't just scatter at random, the signals tend to go in set networks, and these networks form your familiar ways of thinking. This is how this happens. When two brain cells have pulsed their signals at the same time on several occasions, they form a connection so that when one of them now pulses, it's much more likely to make that other one pulse as well. So, after a few repetitions of pulsing together the cells team up into a partnership. In future they are much more likely to signal together, and this means you get to remember something.

All of your memories and your knowledge are formed by these connections between the cell networks. The more you repeat any thought or action, the more these same cells get activated in the same network and the stronger their connection becomes.

Let's take an example. Let's say, every time you have a particularly tough day at work, you buy some biscuits and ice cream on the way home, and sit in front of the TV and eat them.

You have trained the cells in your brain that remember 'it's been a tough day' to connect to 'want some biscuits and ice cream'. That's the memory you have and the connection you strengthen every time you eat this way after a tough day at work.

We all know that repetition is the way we learn, whether learning to write, read, drive or whatever. Even if we just want to remember a phone number or the time of a train we want to catch, we do that by repeating it over and over again.

The interesting part is how you go about making real, lasting changes with this. The key is that when a particular network is no longer reinforced, the cells begin to disconnect. The connections don't disappear instantly but do become weaker and weaker when that particular network of brain cell signalling is no longer reinforced.

So, you might think, why not change your whole routine and go out to a movie whenever you've had a bad day at work? Won't that weaken the connection? You might know from your own experience that it doesn't.

Avoiding a situation, whatever it is, means avoiding the addictive desire connected with that situation, and you don't change the connections this way. I wouldn't be surprised if you've avoided something in the past where you used to overeat, and when you returned to it you also returned to overeating. The reason for this is you never did break that particular connection between that situation and addictive overeating.

In order for the connections to break down, the memory needs to be activated. It's only when that particular network between the cells is active but not reinforced by eating that the connections weaken. They don't change merely through the passing of time. This is why you want to experience your memory of biscuits and ice cream connected to that situation. Perhaps you would notice and manage your desire for them as you pass by the shop where you would have bought them, and again when you're sitting in front of the TV thinking about your lousy day. It's your conscious awareness of the process that makes the crucial difference, so what actually works is to pay attention to your experience of addictive desire so that you actively participate in re-routing the brain signals.

This isn't nearly as difficult or complicated as it may sound. Remember this is happening in our brains anyway as these connections between cells change and reform themselves constantly about all kinds of things. New connections are created in our brains whenever we learn and remember something, and connections are made weaker as we move on in our lives and let go of things that once were hugely significant to us.

A number of psychological issues are treated, successfully, in a very similar way, for example, phobia. This is not to say you have a phobia, just that the process of recovery is similar. People can develop a phobia of almost anything, feeling overwhelmed and even paralysed with fear. This condition is treated is through exposure to the feared object, a bird, for example. The therapist might show their client a drawing of a bird, a photograph and then perhaps a stuffed bird.

Each of those stages will generate fear, and as they allow themselves to feel and accept this fear it begins to fade. In time, they can be close to birds and even touch and feed them. This is because the brain networks that connected 'birds' to 'fear' have weakened, and their phobia is overcome. This is one of the principles behind the standard, cognitive-behavioural therapy (CBT) for phobia, widely used worldwide.

In a very similar way, you expose yourself to your feelings of addictive desire when they occur, whenever you can. When you're feeling your addictive desire to eat, when you want to eat more and you feel unsatisfied, those are the moments when real transformation takes place. This is because you physically change the connections in your brain at that time. There is even research that has demonstrated in a controlled, laboratory setting that a craving for chocolate diminishes when it is *experienced but not satisfied.*

Now, I'm sure you don't need me to tell you there are a great many connections in our brains associated with wanting to eat. If it was just bad days at work, that would be one thing, but we integrate addictive eating into our lives, so there are many things that can trigger connections with food. You can breathe a sigh of relief here, because you don't need to face every single one of these connections in order to weaken them all. You'll work on some and others will seem to take care of themselves. However, there will still be many circumstances you'll meet for the first time, which will trigger a powerful association.

For example, let's say you tend to eat whenever you feel bored. You have established a connection in your brain between feeling bored and eating, so even though you might not feel bored for quite a while, when you do, you'll want to eat. You break this association when you feel bored and you experience and manage your addictive desire. When you allow yourself to feel your unsatisfied desire, those are the moments when you physically rewire that connection between 'I'm bored' and 'I want to eat'. It's not possible to do that if you're not feeling bored. Then, that connection begins to fade. It might not go completely for ever, but it will be considerably less compelling.

Then there are the other connections, say, between overeating and wanting to relax. And wanting to celebrate. And feeling sad. And visiting the local coffee shop (the one where they have those pastries). And walking into your kitchen. And going to the cinema. Etc. Etc. Sometimes you get an addictive desire to eat for no other reason than something just became available. You caught sight of some food, smelled it or simply knew it was there, and now you want to eat it.

All you need to do about all this is continue to live your life as you normally do, and using the themes outlined in Chapters 1,

2 and 3, you develop the habit of noticing and making choices about your addictive desire to eat. It's not essential to identify the cue that triggered it; sometimes it's obvious and sometimes it isn't. It can be a simple thought such as, 'What shall I do now? Oh, I think I'll eat something'. Addictive desire can be triggered by fleeting thoughts and feelings; the slightest annoyance about something or a vague sense of dissatisfaction.

By the way, you don't need to replace the overeating with anything; in fact usually works better if you don't, especially at first. It's not like you're going to get a big hole in your brain where your addictive desire to eat used to be! You simply choose to accept these inevitable feelings of desire instead of satisfying them, and so you weaken them, and so they fade.

Knowing this can make a big difference because it's very common for people to make lots of good changes in their eating, take control of their overeating and do very well for a period of time. Then, perhaps weeks or months later, they encounter a particular circumstance for the first time and they fall back into overeating again. The last time they were in this situation they overate, so there's suddenly a stronger connection, an addictive desire that has yet to fade.

As an example, someone I know, Mary, lives with her family and rarely spends time alone. One day, her family was away visiting a relative while she stayed at home to get some work done. At the end of the day she did a fair bit of addictive overeating. Mary explained it to herself as comfort eating, but another way to explain it is that she had a stronger addictive desire connected to a situation she hadn't come across for a long time. She used to overeat quite a lot when she was single, many years ago. It's not that her feelings about spending one evening on her own were so unbearable. In fact, she said she quite enjoyed having some time to herself. It's just that this situation triggered her memory, her addictive desire. Had she accepted this desire and not fed it, it too would have faded in time, even when she was on her own.

Unfortunately, it usually gets satisfied and reinforced, and what also gets reinforced is the sense of utter powerlessness to control eating in certain circumstances. So people say, 'I was doing fine until I went on holiday' or 'until I got stressed at work' or 'until I broke up with my boyfriend' or 'until I stayed at home all day with the kids'. Just remember that all of these present nothing other than more brain connections to be redesigned. As you go through these experiences in your life and no longer reinforce their connections with overeating, they fade.

Now, there's something else about how brains work that's very helpful to know. To put this as simply as possible, when your addictive desire to eat is triggered, this desire comes from the middle part of your brain, roughly in between your ears. This is a more primitive area, one that deals with very basic survival instincts. If you feel consumed with addictive desire, overwhelmed by it and driven mad with it, this mid-brain area is dominating your thinking. You could feel like you really will die if you don't binge on biscuits and ice cream, and there's absolutely no reasoning with it.

In order to bring a more sane perspective to this more intense desire, another part of the brain needs to be brought into play, and this is right at the front of your brain, just behind your forehead. Called the prefrontal cortex (PFC), this is a more highly developed area; the most adaptable part of the brain and it's the part that's the most evolved. The more you use it, the more it will calm down that mid-brain desire.

We have just looked at breaking down networks of cell communication, and in a similar way it's important to strengthen connections between the mid-brain and the PFC. As before, this requires deliberate, conscious repetition *while the addictive desire is happening.*

Researchers using brain-scanning technology studied the function of the PFC in addicted drug users in a rehab clinic. They recorded how much each person used their PFC in simple choice-making tasks; those with greater activity turned out to be those who stayed off drugs long term.

Another study looked at women who had lost at least 30 pounds and maintained that weight loss for at least a year. Monitoring brain function while they ate a meal, they had greater PFC activity than a control group with no successful weight loss.

When the PFC becomes extremely damaged through serious physical injury, people lose all control of any impulse they may have. This kind of injury compels people to follow through on any whim that flips through their mind, and with impulses ruling absolutely, life is chaotic and relationships impossible. This is because they have no ability to reason with themselves, to have any consideration at all that some actions might not be wise.

But doctors have found that even physical damage to the brain can be repaired. This is carried out, not through surgery, but through the brain rebuilding itself. Doctors who specialise in brain rehabilitation, after accidents or strokes for example, have found two things are required: *paying attention* and *repetition*.

So, the more you deliberately manage your experience of addictive desire, at any opportunity, the more you activate and strengthen this area of your brain.

Inasmuch as you have difficulty with food, you have trained yourself not to control one particular kind of impulse, the impulse to overeat. This training may have continued for years and may even have begun in childhood before you had any idea what was happening. It wasn't a physical injury that impaired this particular brain function, but the effects are similar because you're not using the PFC, just as if it was physically disabled.

There are three main concepts to bring to mind that will develop connections with the PFC. You will recognise them from our previous chapters.

1. Declare your own freedom of choice in the matter, 'I am free to eat anything I can get my hands on, any time.' If you don't assert this in your mind you are likely to assume a prohibitive, diet mentality by default. Research has shown that people don't use the PFC when they are following instructions or set routines.

2. Choose the outcome you'll create by considering how you expect to feel after you've finished overeating. You activate your PFC when you think beyond the immediate pleasure of eating, and include the outcome as well. This is where you can recall that list you started making after reading Chapter 2.

3. Use words in your mind to name what's happening, 'This is an addictive desire to eat.' Research shows that simply putting words to a feeling lessens the strength of the mid-brain while increasing activity in the PFC. It's deceptively simple, but getting into the habit of naming your addictive desire is a huge step forward. Then, of course, you remember that when you satisfy it by overeating, you reinforce it and keep it alive.

Even though it may take real effort to focus on these three themes, every time you do you will be building your capacity to manage and tame your addictive appetite through increasing activity in your prefrontal cortex.

The aim of this chapter is to help you to understand what's actually happening when you work with this approach. Then, you're not blindly following orders, following directions just because I've told you to. You're using the principles because you understand them, because you know what you're doing.

We have been looking at the ways in which the brain changes, physically, by the ways in which you think. This is useful for two reasons.

One, to understand that our familiar thoughts and actions are physically etched into our brains, and that's why we tend to get stuck in ruts of habitual behaviour. They really are like ruts or grooves, and it takes some effort to get out of them.

The second thing is that this isn't permanent; these grooves can be changed with some persistence. So you can accept the reality that these familiar networks are there, and at the same time begin to make choices to do things differently, knowing that in time and with practice things will get easier. They'll get easier because you'll be creating a new brain.

In general, you either strengthen the connections in your brain or you weaken them – every day, with every encounter with food. Does this sound rather daunting? Well, the best thing about it all is that there's room for error. Don't get the idea that everything rests on the next piece of chocolate you are (or are not?) going to eat!

You may still want to be impulsive around food sometimes,

and that's fine. I'm assuming you are way too impulsive around food and you have a tough time controlling that. The odd moments don't matter so much. If you just get better at redesigning these connections, you'll do fine. Doing this in an imperfect way is something we'll look at in our next chapter.

WHAT YOU CAN DO

▸ Don't necessarily avoid the situations in which you overeat. They are not problems but opportunities for you to make genuine changes.

▸ You don't need to make changes all at once. Take your time. See what overeating you really do want to change and be clear about why you want to change it. In time you may want to develop new routines, but it will be best to do this having first made peace with your addictive desire to eat. Then, when you fall back into your old ways – and who doesn't every now and then? – you won't necessarily fall back into a binge.

▸ Take a couple of deep, slow breaths as you start to work through your addictive desire to eat. This will bring down your level of stress and this, too, improves access to the PFC.

▸ Pay attention to what you're doing when you expose yourself to feelings of temptation and desire. The more you actively attend to this process, the better results you get.

▸ The connections between cell networks are stronger when emotions are involved. This is why you may find that your desire to eat is more persistent when triggered by feelings such as anger or sadness.

▸ If you substitute another addictive behaviour, such as smoking, drinking alcohol or shopping, in the place of eating, you will continue to reinforce the same networks, keeping them in business. This is known as 'cross addiction' or 'addiction transfer'. It is not so much a problem of trading in one addiction for another, as much as it's adding or increasing the strength of another addiction.

The solution is to regard any extra addictive desire as different forms of the same desire, working through it as if it was an addictive desire to eat.

▸ However, it's very likely that there will be times when a substitution is entirely appropriate, and not necessarily addictive. For example, if you snack on chocolate in the afternoons you might want to eat some fruit instead, if you don't normally do that.

▸ Be willing to be repetitive. The patterns in brain activation do change, but not instantaneously. It pays to be patient. Remember how many years you have been overeating, so don't expect your memory of this to vanish like magic.

▸ Ask yourself the three questions:

> Am I choosing?
> Why does it matter?
> How am I responding to temptation?

IRIS'S STORY

The seminar raised a lot of awareness and I think the key lesson that remains is awareness of addiction. If you have a situation where you overeat and you remove the overeating from the situation, you create a vacuum. I had always been aware of that but I had never known what to do about it.

Whatever I did; get busy, exercise, socialise, the vacuum was always there. Now for the first time I have a name for it: it's my addictive desire to eat. That's been the big revelation for me, because naming it like that has stripped away all the extra bits and pieces I added to it and attributed to it. It used to mean I was incomplete, immature and somehow different from everybody else. At least, that's what I made it mean but I can easily see now that it's just a memory of something I used to do. That realisation has changed so much for me and continues to do so.

I had been pregnant while I did the seminar and I wanted to do the best for my children and do the best for me. Even though I was enormous, it was because I was carrying twins and not because I had been pigging out!

The seminar reinforced my healthy attitude. Without it I would have used pregnancy as an excuse to overeat, because nobody would know the difference. But I was aware whenever I ate: why was I eating this? I'm more aware of the excuses I would give myself and I realised that pregnancy was a wonderful excuse: 'I'm eating for three!'

CHAPTER FIVE

GIVE YOURSELF A BREAK

So far we've looked at how to change the way you think about eating. With this approach you'll have control at your fingertips – instead of chocolate and cake crumbs! You'll make progress through persistence, and through getting to the truth of your answers to those three questions. You gain greater control as you become more aware of the thinking that drives your behaviour.

However, there are some issues you may bring to this process, which can block your progress. When you understand what they are you'll be able to notice and overcome them. Then you continue unhampered, working towards developing more control over what and how much you eat.

The obstacles we'll look at are guilt, fear and perfectionism. You might encounter one of these as a problem or two of them or all three. Often they go hand in hand, so you might need to deal with each one to some extent.

GUILT can be a valuable emotion provided it doesn't last too long, dragging you down into chronic self-hatred. The reason guilt can be a valuable response to overeating is because it's a sign you're doing something self-destructive. If you wrecked somebody else's health, or if you kept lying or breaking your word to somebody else, you would expect to feel a bit guilty about that, wouldn't you? Behaving in that way means that a certain amount of guilt is appropriate. It's telling you something, and all you need to do is to listen and see how you want to respond to what it's saying.

Guilt, however, becomes a serious obstacle when it's severe. Then you feel very guilty most of the time, possibly about pretty much everything, but especially about your eating and almost certainly about how your body looks. Extreme, unrelenting guilt blocks your progress because it keeps you stuck in lower self-esteem. It takes some effort to change this because you start out with little or no confidence in and regard for yourself.

This kind of self-hatred is often strongest when it's directed at body size, keeping you locked into weight loss as the only reason you would want to eat less. Perhaps you improve your eating for a while in an attempt to lose weight. Maybe you lose a bit and maybe you don't, but it's a slow process. Your self-hatred is still there, so it's easy for your motivation to fade. Then, it's often a case of, 'what the heck, I'm fat anyway so why not go ahead and eat everything I want'. Whether you are eating less or not, your choices are all about the way you look.

It could be that appearance matters to you most because it's what everybody else sees and makes their judgments about. But your harshest judge is probably you, and this is what keeps you from making real changes.

You can begin to change things, as we saw in Chapter 2, by addressing the cause of the problem rather than the effect. Then you can recognise that extra weight is just *one* of the effects created by your overeating and that there are many others. Mostly, those other effects, such as health and self-esteem, have a very private impact on you and you alone. And that's what makes them so significant. Starting to care more about yourself can be the switch that begins to make all the difference.

At first it may feel as if you are *pretending* to care about yourself. It may not seem genuine, because it's so different. It's a 'new you' because you start out with lower self-esteem.

With lower self-esteem, overeating may be a way to punish yourself. You overeat in a self-destructive way, knowing full well that you'll regret it later on. You don't like yourself, so you have little interest in being kind to yourself. This can keep you helpless, anxious and even depressed. Your overeating generates more guilt and lowers your self-esteem even more.

This toxic guilt can become a way of life, and overeating isn't necessarily the only aspect of your life it touches, although eating and weight may be central. The vicious circle is: 'I'm fat and worthless so I might as well eat more, so I overeat and then I get fatter and feel even more guilty, which proves I'm worthless, so I might as well eat some more…'

If you recognise yourself here, you could be one of those extremely capable people who cover up their self-loathing with an over-committed, people-pleasing lifestyle. You rarely take time for yourself because you always put others first. If someone pays you a compliment, you find some way to invalidate it. If someone steps on your foot, you're the one who apologises. You find it tough to say 'no' and maybe allow yourself to be walked over like a doormat. You rarely think of yourself, only of others. The chances are you've even been reading this book with someone else in mind.

Of course it's not a bad thing to look after people and to put others first. But think of the advice given aboard an airliner in the event of a drop in cabin pressure, when oxygen masks are released. Even if you are travelling with your own children: first, you put on your own oxygen mask, then help others with theirs.

It's really a question of finding a balance. If you never attend to your own needs, then that balance is not in your own best interests. It may not even be in the best interests of the people who depend on you.

If this is even close to your style, see if you use guilt as a stick to beat yourself up. Maybe you think that if you make yourself feel bad enough, you won't binge any more. You may fear that if you eased up on the guilt and forgave yourself a bit, you'd never stop eating. But it doesn't work that way – and you know it doesn't, don't you?

Forgiving yourself doesn't make you apathetic. Having some compassion for yourself doesn't mean you then never want anything to change. In fact the reverse is true. If you wanted a child to develop in some way, to face his fears and try something new and challenging, you know instinctively that patience, recognition and unconditional love are what will support that child most. It's the same with the support you give to yourself!

The antidote to exaggerated guilt is forgiveness. Forgiveness is a choice you can make by getting in touch with the spirit in you, who exists quite apart from anything you do and anything you happen to look like. Forgiveness is about claiming your essential worth as a human being.

I usually find that those people who feel the most guilty about their eating are not owning their choices. I have often seen that guilt is the feeling that goes along with the belief, 'I'm not allowed to eat like this.' As you begin to work with the themes in this book, you will begin to see your choices more clearly and be able to make the choices that you are prepared to live with. As a result, guilt lessens.

FEAR comes in many forms. FEAR OF FAILURE may be inevitable to some degree, but for many it can seem not so much a fear as a certainty. Many people get so used to losing control of their eating that they have long ago resigned themselves to the way things are, giving up all possibility of any lasting change.

They may at times go through some half-hearted motions of trying, in a sort of dreamy state of, 'I really should do something about this'. Their deep resignation, though, means they won't put any real effort into it. If they really went for it and failed yet again it would be too disappointing, so it's not worth the risk. So they make petty attempts at some superficial changes, fail (of course!) and resign themselves once again to the out of control norm. Usually something else gets blamed in this process, at least partly. So it becomes a case of, 'I would have stuck to it, but my family … but my job … but my love of food got in the way.' This is how a fear of failure actually creates failure! It's a self-fulfilling prophecy.

Recognising this fear is a good place to start, so it's helpful to admit that you fear you'll fail. This, of course, requires some courage because you're acting in the face of fear, not in its absence. This is good, and you want to set your sights high enough so that some of your fear of failure appears. Aim high, but not purely in terms of weight loss. Chapter 7 may help you to find some other targets. Then you get involved, putting as much effort and time and energy and attention into it as you can, even in the face of your conviction that it will never work. And guess what will happen then? You'll fail!

Let me explain. You see, there's failure and there's failure, and a certain amount of failure is inevitable. Not only is it to be expected, but failure is an essential part of learning. I was delighted when I found out that this idea was made famous by Thomas Edison. Often regarded as the greatest inventor ever, Edison was the first to record sound, invented the electric light bulb, and took out over 1,000 patents. Most people would regard him as successful.

Throughout it all, he saw failure as part of the process. I can imagine him saying to himself, 'well, that's another way not to make a light bulb... and that's another way...' And so on, until he got it right and the light bulb worked. I want to suggest that his positive relationship with failure was the key to his success. If he had let his failures get on top of him, he wouldn't have got there in the end.

To Edison, failure simply meant that there was something to learn, and it can mean that to you too. So any time you fail, you either you give up trying or you look to see what there is for you to learn. Failure isn't the problem; it's how you respond to failure that determines your success in the long term.

FEAR OF SUCCESS, however, can be just as much of an obstacle for those with low self-esteem. This is because not only will you expect to fail, but failure will seem familiar, comfortable and safe. Success at anything can be frightening and some people fear they might change too much, in ways they don't like and can't handle. Many very successful people with lower self-esteem sabotage themselves some significant way, and often this is with overeating or other addictions.

Cope with this fear by taking things as they come, reminding yourself that you always have the freedom to return to overeating. It's up to you: if you don't like being in control of what you eat and all it means, you don't have to stick with it!

What makes all the difference is moving your motivation away from appearance and towards health. If all you care about is 'looking good', this tends to reinforce low self-esteem. Wanting the best of health reinforces high self-esteem. I expect that both are involved in your choices about food, but usually one of these types of motivation dominates.

Prioritise health, and as your self-esteem improves, your tendency to self-sabotage lessens. Higher self-esteem means you become less self-conscious and less sensitive to criticism, you feel more at ease and at more peace with yourself, more creative, productive and enthusiastic about life in general. In other words, you discover in time that there's not really too much to fear.

FEAR OF NATURAL HUNGER often results from years of dieting. Following a diet is guaranteed to create a strong sense of deprivation, so whenever natural hunger surfaces, it's met with anxiety and even panic because you are 'not allowed' to satisfy it.

Many people overeat so that they can be absolutely sure they won't feel hungry before they will be eating again. To some extent this makes sense, but it's very much a matter of degree. If you fear hunger so much that you must never feel it at all, you'll find it tough to eat less.

As with any fear, the way to overcome it is by facing it. Make sure some food is always available so that you know you are choosing to feel your hunger, and for how long you feel it. It would be best to keep food with you that is nourishing and not quite so attractive and compelling as more addictive food. Then, gradually allow yourself to move towards feeling your natural hunger. You don't need to skip meals in order to do this but perhaps eat less at your meals and have fewer snacks in between.

Natural hunger isn't a bad thing; it's a signal to eat something soon. It's perfectly normal and natural to feel it sometimes, it comes and goes, and it's not completely unpleasant. (If it's physically painful, it would be wise to see a doctor about that.) As much as you can, discover the difference between natural hunger and your addictive desire to eat. This can take time, and as we've already seen it's not completely reliable, but it can be valuable to identify natural hunger and be willing to feel it sometimes.

FEAR OF THE ADDICTIVE DESIRE TO EAT is very common because it can seem to overwhelm you and force you to overeat, despite your best efforts. This means you are likely to fight it and find it impossible to accept. As we saw in Chapter 3, when you fight it, it fights back, so the more you want it to go away, the more it's going to be there and the more it will seem to be a problem.

You can overcome this fear if you remember this: your feeling of desire, uncomfortable as it is, doesn't make you overeat. You overeat because you want the feeling of unsatisfied desire to go away. Whenever you do some addictive eating, the desire becomes satisfied at some point, and then it's gone, at least for a while. You feel 'normal' again, but you've just gone through another binge.

By letting yourself accept your feeling of desire, you gain the ability to be in control. While you feel this desire, you are not overeating as a direct result – and if you keep this in mind you will lose your fear of it. If you're afraid of the dark you turn on a light, so shine a light on your addictive desire to eat and take a good look at it. When you do you'll see there are no monsters there, just an uncomfortable feeling of unsatisfied desire which will pass in time.

PERFECTIONISM can be a way of thinking about almost every-thing, certainly more than just about food. It shows up in those niggling thoughts that no matter what you achieve, you should have done better. With food, you either maintain a rigid control of your eating, with not a bite out of place, or you eat in a way that's completely indulgent with no real attempt to take any control at all. For a perfectionist, it's all or it's nothing.

Perfectionism makes it almost impossible to stay motivated long term because any time any one thing is out of place, it's all completely invalidated. If it's not 100 per cent perfect, it's 100 per cent rubbish. Perfectionists zero in on the one thing that's wrong and that one thing becomes everything. It becomes the evidence that you're not good enough and maybe never will be.

Many perfectionists associate eating 'perfectly' with living 'perfectly'. For periods of time their eating is healthy and in control, and their home is tidy and clean, the bed gets made every day, clothes get picked up and the cat gets fed. Some people will tie in trips to the gym or abstaining from alcohol. Then, one thing goes wrong and it all goes wrong.

For many perfectionists, there's something hugely enjoyable about the 'perfect' phase. It generates a powerful 'high', a sense of exhilaration and energy that's extremely attractive. There's also a downside, though, and that can be an almost constant anxiety that it won't last.

And of course it doesn't last and it never will. It's a very tall order for anyone to stay in control of addictive overeating perfectly. In the first place, it's impossible to define 'perfect eating'. The very idea conjures up silly questions such as, 'how many peas do I need for optimum health?'

We can only make our best, educated guesses at what we need to eat each day. Therefore, a definition of addictive overeating can only be approximate. It's only possible to say whether or not you overeat in terms of degree: either 'a great deal' or 'not very much' or somewhere in between.

The biggest problem with perfectionism, though, is that it's usually carried out by denying free choice. A perfectionist's way of eating is so rigid that there's no room for error, so the sense of prohibition is inevitable and strong. Remember from Chapter 1 that it's possible to comply with restrictions for a while but eventually this way of thinking sets up rebellious overeating – and you are back where you started. Not only that, but while the 'regime' is being followed, it feels like you are depriving or denying yourself.

Keeping to a rigid regime is anti-social, inconvenient, stressful and often obsessive. To make matters even worse, after the regime is broken and overeating resumed, it's very tough to get back into control because it was so restrictive and negative. This is a main cause of procrastination when it comes to making healthy changes in eating.

All you need to do about this is, instead of aiming for 100 per cent perfection, aim for success in terms of degrees. Eliminate absolute success and you eliminate absolute failure at the same time. Get a picture of all the overeating you do when you're in your out of control phase, and call that 100 per cent addictive eating for you. If you then ate 10 or 20 per cent of that, that would be a pretty good result, wouldn't it? That's what you want to aim for. Then you can say, for example, 'I'm successfully in control of my eating about 80 per cent of the time'. Which is a lot better than nothing! Then you can acknowledge your successes, so then you can stay motivated.

Simply stop aiming for perfection. You don't need it in order to succeed. It's not perfection that leads you to success in the long term. What leads to your success is your ability to deal with your addictive desire to eat. When you have developed that skill, then, even when you do eat in an addictive way, you can easily get back into control.

WHAT YOU CAN DO

▸ Whenever you forgive yourself for some overeating you've done, follow it with an action to back it up. Find a symbolic act of self-nurturing that's a little bit of a challenge. Perhaps you eat some fruit if you don't often do that, or choose to accept an addictive desire to eat something sugary. Eating something healthy can be every bit as positive a move in the right direction as not eating something that undermines your health.

▶   Self-hatred in the context we're looking at here is usually hatred of physical appearance. One place to start with this is to remember that you aren't just a body, but also mind and spirit. When you can really appreciate your non-physical aspects, you'll be more able to honour your physical self as well by eating in a healthier way. Love your spirit first, and allow that love to seep into your mind. Then, choices will follow more naturally that will develop a body to reflect that self-love.

▶   Let go of black-and-white, all-or-none thinking, thinking instead in terms of shades of grey or percentages. Aim for 80 per cent or whatever seems to work for you. If that's too high, aim for 50 per cent and keep looking for ways to improve on that.

▶   Be willing to give up the high of perfection. Whenever you're in one of your 'perfect' phases, deliberately eat in a way that's imperfect. Mess it up, here and there. You'll lose the thrill of perfection, but you'll also lose those plunges into the nightmare, out of control eating when it all falls apart. Know that 'perfect' eating is completely unnecessary, either for weight loss or optimum health.

▶   What percentage of success did you have with your eating today? Acknowledge one thing you did or didn't eat that you are pleased about.

MAGGIE

There have been many benefits I've received from doing this seminar, but there's one that surprised me and this one has been a real joy. The reason it surprised me is because I had become so accustomed to the constant complaining in my head, a sort of whining to myself in the background or sometimes in the foreground of my thoughts, but never going away for very long. I was continually moaning to myself about what I ate and how I looked and how it wasn't at all like I wanted it to be. It was like going through life with someone whispering in your ear, 'you're a failure' every minute of every day. It was only when I noticed it had gone that I realised it had been there, if you know what I mean. I don't think it's gone completely, I should say, but it's quite different now.

I did not like the idea of eating being an addiction, so that took some getting used to. It seemed much too judgmental and harsh. But it did give me a way to get out of this mental whining that things are not like how you want them. It comes down to that fact that you can't continue to justify overeating and stop overeating at the same time. It sounds so obvious now that I'm writing this down, but that's what you really want, isn't it? You want the best of both worlds: overeating without any of the bad consequences. So the thing was to ask myself if this really is the way I wanted to live, and am I likely to get the consequences I'd want to live with later on.

The thing I find most helpful is planning your meal before you start eating and I always do this with my evening meal. I have a little conversation with myself, checking if this really is what I want to eat and how much. I'm clear about it before I start eating and then I can be clear about it when I've stopped, because I always want to go on after I've finished. So then I think, that's what the addiction wants to eat, it's not what I want.

CHAPTER SIX

I OVEREAT BECAUSE...

It has often been said that when it comes to overeating, it's not what you eat, it's why you eat that's the key. Why you overeat, for example, is because you're sad, maybe even depressed, and you know that eating something sugary and creamy will comfort you and cheer you up.

Another example might be that you overeat because it brings you pleasure, and after a hard day at work, when you perhaps feel unappreciated, you think you deserve a nice treat of something really yummy to help you to unwind.

This way of thinking is very common, of course, and at first glance may seem to completely explain everything about why people overeat. But there's a problem with it, and this is that most people's experience is that the comfort and pleasure they enjoy from addictive overeating is rather short-lived. It usually lasts, as if I need to tell you, for the time it takes to eat the treat, and sometimes not even that. Of course, you could treat yourself by eating all day long, but there's a significant cost to that, in terms of self-esteem and health – not to mention wealth!

For many, their upset about overeating and being overweight is so great that there's little comfort in any eating at all. Even when it's brief, the comfort and pleasure is then most often followed by its opposite: some degree of psychological and physical upset, discomfort and regret.

If someone offered to give you some money but in half an hour they would get double the amount back, I imagine you wouldn't be too impressed with the deal. So why do so many people continue to fall for a similar con? We all know that depressed people who eat loads of chocolate every day don't become any happier as a result. Stressed people who constantly snack on rubbish don't feel less stressed as a result. Bored people could easily find any number of things to do with their time, other than overeat. We tell ourselves that overeating is enhancing our life – while at the same time knowing that it is impairing and could even be destroying it.

The way to understand this paradox is to understand the addictive desire to eat. When you have an addictive desire, for something sugary for example, a primitive survival system is being activated in your brain. Dopamine, a chemical in your brain, is being released, which takes over your thinking and keeps you focussed on getting some food into your mouth.

This survival mechanism got put in place at a time when there wasn't a great deal of food around, and especially no sugar or manufactured products. So it is unable to distinguish between a healthy need for cabbage, say, and a box of donuts.

You are being driven by that ancient survival system whenever you feel your addictive desire to eat, and part of that system shows up as very persuasive and credible reasoning. You are in an altered state of consciousness, which can for some people seem like a trance, where food is all that matters.

Fat, salt and the high glycemic-load carbohydrates, such as sugar and wheat, activate this survival mechanism more powerfully. Not because they are healthy, but because of the stronger biochemical rewards they activate.

This is why you love them so much and this is why they have the quality of being more addictive. Your ancient brain thinks they are essential for life, when in fact they are the opposite. (All food activates this reward system to some extent, which is why it's possible to overeat healthy foods, such as vegetables.)

Your addictive desire demands to be satisfied, but even though all that activity is going on in your brain, you can be quite unaware of it. For most people, all they are aware of is they keep eating too much - and sometimes they aren't even aware of that!

Of course people don't notice that a cue has triggered a burst of dopamine in their brain, so they react automatically, in a fairly unconscious state. Often, all they are aware of is how they are persuading themselves to eat: I'm bored, sad, in need of comfort, stressed, lonely – or whatever.

This is how you explain your overeating, to make sense of what you're doing. But it's not boredom, sadness or stress that causes the overeating. It's because those are the circumstances in which you feel – and satisfy – your addictive desire. And the addictive desire means that dopamine is in your brain, insisting that you could die if you don't eat something right now.

Understanding this helps to make a great deal of sense of things. This is why you can overeat when you're depressed but also when you're happy, when you're celebrating, when you're lonely, when you're busy and when you're relaxing.

The truth is people overeat in lots of different circumstances. Their explanation simply matches whatever happens to be going on at the time.

This is why examining your feelings, although a fine thing to do, will only produce limited success with overeating. Feeling frustrated and angry about something could trigger your desire to eat. By all means investigate those feelings and see what you want to do about the frustrating situation. Just know that this doesn't necessarily cancel out your addictive desire.

This is why, when we need comforting, it's not enough to

take a candle-lit bath, listen to music, spend some time with a loved pet or any of hundreds of other things we could do restore our spirits. If feeling comforted were truly our aim, these things would work fine. But none of these things satisfy our addictive desire to eat.

When you begin to notice how you persuade yourself to satisfy your addictive desire to eat, you might see flimsy excuses that no longer hold water for you. But sometimes your reasons can seem, well, entirely justifiable. It can be that you overeat a great deal, not because your addictive desire is so intense and unacceptable, but because you've got some very compelling justifications for satisfying it.

This could be because you're overwhelmed by feelings here and now or because traumatic events happened in your past. The trauma may have passed long ago, but it's remembered, even briefly from time to time, and this becomes a persistent and very credible reason to satisfy your addictive desire: 'Such-and-such happened to me in the past, so I'm going to go ahead and eat.'

No doubt you call that comfort eating; who wouldn't? You have these bad memories and so you comfort yourself with food. That sounds reasonable, doesn't it? Yes it does, but another way to explain it is that you have an addictive desire to eat, and you habitually justify satisfying it (reinforcing it at the same time) by thinking of these events. You have a free pass to all the eating you ever want to do, and nobody would blame you, including yourself.

It certainly may help you to explore these painful memories, perhaps with the support of a therapist, and gain benefit from that. But if you have already done that and you are still overeating, it's because you haven't taken the next step. This is to refuse to use this justification any more and start to make choices to accept – and not to satisfy – your addictive desire. You decide that, yes, these dreadful things happened to you, but you don't want to continue to use them to support your overeating.

It's a common idea that those who overeat carry some deep wound that needs to be healed, but that isn't necessarily the best way to see it. Sometimes people start to overeat because of some difficulty in their lives, but when the difficulty has passed (and perhaps completely resolved) the addictive relationship with food persists, simply because the addictive desire continues to be fed and reinforced.

Especially in tough times, it can seem like a miracle not to overeat, but this can be the one thing in your life you can find delight in at that time. There are a great many things in life that you have absolutely no control of and no choice about – but it's great to know that your eating doesn't have to be one of them!

Your biggest breakthroughs will occur when you discover that difficult emotions don't get any worse when you don't overeat. If this has happened in the past, it's because you were not managing your addictive desire well. When it's not managed effectively, you can feel worse because you feel deprived; you get strong cravings and feel overwhelmed with feelings of self-sacrifice.

This changes when you take on board that it's always your choice. When you are denying freedom of choice, operating in that state of deprivation, you will attach yourself much more strongly to your justifications. They become crucial because they provide you with the freedom to overeat that you so desperately need. Embracing a real sense of choice means seeing that you can choose to eat whatever you want. Then, those justifications lose their grip.

Remember that when you make a choice, you choose the outcome as well. So if you choose comfort and pleasure, also choose what it will cost you: fatigue, perhaps, and feeling out of control. It could also strengthen a sense of victimhood by reinforcing the belief, 'Not only did he/she/it make me feel bad, but they made me overeat as well.' The first step out of this could be to disentangle 'they made me overeat as well' from that scenario. This is a step towards stronger self-esteem and control of overeating.

Many of the excuses you give yourself will simply fall away when you realise that all you're really doing is satisfying an addictive desire to eat. If it's really worth it to you, you won't follow through on the addictive desire even when you've got the best excuse in the world. If it's worth it to you. When you connect with the improved quality of life you get as a result of taking control of your eating, then you can say, 'I either have this miserable situation in my life and I overeat or I have this miserable situation in my life and I don't overeat.'

And really, what's the difference? The only real difference is whether or not the addictive desire is satisfied. The illusion is that overeating helps you cope with the situation, but the reverse is more likely to be true. Staying in control of your eating brings you more confidence and higher self-esteem, and this will support you through tough times far more than overeating ever can. The key here is to be willing to accept and manage the uncomfortable feeling of desire, even when everything else is going badly.

Remember from Chapters 3 and 4 that your addictive desire to eat will fade when it's managed but not satisfied. The memory of overeating simply plays itself out until a new memory is formed, one where you're in that situation and you don't think about overeating. Then you have the crisis, you have the difficult emotions, and you deal with it all the best you can. You find ways to comfort yourself and restore your sense of hope and optimism about yourself and your life. And overeating doesn't come into it at all.

In the past you may have simply tried to avoid the upsets in your life, in the hope that your addictive desire will disappear. Sometimes this works for a while, but difficulties tend to be a part of all our lives. For most of us, the moments are rare when we feel perfectly balanced, at peace with the world and only interested in a salad for lunch.

WHAT YOU CAN DO

▶   Notice the justification you give yourself next time you overeat. If you find it difficult to identify, delay satisfying your addictive desire for a while and it will become clearer and more urgent. Just like somebody trying to attract your attention.

You might notice more than one justification at a time, and you probably use only a few over and over again. These few are your favourites; convincing, reasonable standbys you can always count on to get the food into your mouth.

▶   There is no limit to the ways addictive overeating can be justified. You might think, for example, 'This is just how I am, someone with no willpower who eats everything in sight.' Or maybe you're fond of telling yourself, 'Just one little bite won't make any difference.' It's amazing how much you can eat with this one!

▶   It's tough to stay aware of this all the time, so you may miss some of the justifications and overeat. Don't worry if it's just now and again. But if it's happening often, look for the justification you keep using and see what you can do about it. When you're too attached to your justifications too much of the time, it will be tough to manage the feeling of desire without eating.

▸ Managing your addictive desire to eat can take place in the supermarket, when you walk down the aisles and hear your favourite goodies calling out to you. In a sense, you make a choice to eat those foods when you choose to buy them. If you don't buy them, you won't be eating them.

If you 'buy them for others' but usually end up eating them yourself, be honest with yourself about that, and choose what you really want to do. It's fine to leave them there in the shops.

▸ If you often buy addictive food for others, you might want to ask yourself why you are doing that. Do you really want to perpetuate this problem in your own community or start to solve it? See if you can find healthier options to offer your family and friends. Healthier options usually don't have that addictive 'kick' to them, so they aren't as attractive and compelling.

▸ If lack of money is your favourite justification for eating manufactured food, please understand that in terms of nutrition (rather than addiction) you are much better off eating real food. Processing, packaging, advertising and marketing all cost a great deal of money, so that's what you're really paying for.

People spend their working lives creating slogans such as '95% fat free' for something that's mostly sugar, and 'made with olive oil' for a sauce that's mostly vegetable oil. Who pays their wages? You?

▸ You've started, so why not continue? If what you've read of this book so far has made sense to you but you haven't put it into practice yet, look to see how you are justifying that. Too busy? Doesn't feel right? Keep forgetting about it? Your resistance is unlikely to go away, so if you leave this book on a shelf it could mean it will stay there for a very long time.

LESLEY'S STORY

It's a cliché but it's true to say that I've tried every diet in the book. And they all worked wonderfully. The problem was that I could never stick to any of them for any length of time. I'd start off feeling determined, full of expectations and excitement, believing this to be the one that would finally streamline my massive thighs and hips without leaving me feeling resentful and grumpy from self-denial and hunger. But within a week or two, usually when I was particularly tired, upset or pre-menstrual, I'd slip back to my old comfort eating, justifying it with a library of personal excuses for why I 'deserved a treat', or 'needed a lift' or whatever. What I hadn't grasped was that as soon as I went on any form of diet I was doomed to failure.

It took a while for it to really sink in and for me to view the whole 'desire' thing as a positive opportunity. I found that the more I looked forward to the addictive desire hitting me, so to speak, in order to confront it and work through it, the less powerful it was. My familiar situations, incidentally, were never physical situations for me, such as craving biscuits with coffee or desert after a meal. It was always emotional states that triggered my desire; whenever I felt particularly tired, fat, fed up, ugly, etc.

And now I truly believe I have the power to face all these negative emotional states without the need to throw high fat, high sugar food into my mouth in order to deal with it. This, for me, is what is so very extraordinary about this approach.

This has quite literally given me back my self-esteem, my ability to choose what to eat and when to eat it, and the freedom to go where I want and do what I want without being afraid of food. Since attending the seminar I have thrown out the thirty or so 'healthy eating' books I had on my shelf and turned my back on dieting forever. I now choose good, nutritious food, I have great self-esteem and I feel really in control of the one area of my life that has caused me so many problems over the years. Oh yes, and I've lost about 30 pounds.

CHAPTER SEVEN

THE GOOD STUFF

I'm sure you don't need me to tell you there's a massive amount of information available about healthy eating. Some of it is contradictory, and I expect there will always be some amount of controversy in the field of nutrition. However, there has been so much research done now, that some basic principles are very reliably established as to how to eat for the best of health.

The basis of these recommendations is very simple: the more whole, plant foods you eat, the better. By whole, I mean that you mostly look for things to eat that look like real plants. Aim to eat more vegetables and some fruit, in their fairly natural states, rather than processed and manufactured. For many people, this also means eating considerably less sugar, wheat, fat/oil and any products that come from animals.

The difficulty with this is not that there is much serious controversy over this advice or the reasons for it. The difficulty is that when people come across advice such as this, they usually think of it as a set of rules that must be obeyed. They think this advice threatens to prohibit their favourite addictive overeating, so that they will have to deprive themselves of their treats.

Then, the advice is challenged, ignored and persistently compromised in hundreds of ways. For example, if someone noticed a few limp slices of green pepper on a double-cheese pepperoni pizza, and convinced themselves they were eating a portion of vegetables!

It is crucial to remember, first of all, that you are totally free to eat anything you want, as much of it as you want, any time. It's only when you really see that you've got this option that it's possible to begin to make genuine choices to do something else. As you know from our first few chapters, making choices involves recognising our desire for the addictive, unhealthy 'foods' and re-evaluating this desire given that there are benefits that come from eating less of them.

Now, if you aren't seeing any benefits coming from changes you've made, it will be tougher to continue with it because it will seem a huge effort for very little reward. Remember from Chapter 2 that losing weight isn't the best way to motivate yourself, partly because it is a slow process. What's better is to look for things such as increases in energy and vitality, being free from acid indigestion, or improvements in mood and self-esteem that come from eating healthier food. So it's important to make enough of the right kinds of changes so that you can appreciate the point of it all, so that you can feel and stay motivated. As a simple example, you could use what you've learned in this book to eat one fast-food cheeseburger instead of two for lunch every day. You might see an immediate benefit in that, but not nearly as much as if you'd had bowl of homemade bean and vegetable soup.

There are very good reasons for this. As the soup is likely to be less convenient and less desirable (that is, not so addictive), it will be important to grasp these reasons.

First, understand that the healthy – and considerably more sustainable – way to lose weight is to lose storage fat, while maintaining and even building lean mass. The more lean mass you have, the better, and that's what a largely plant-based diet can deliver. The more lean mass you have, the younger you are, biologically speaking, and the higher your metabolic rate, meaning you burn calories faster. The more lean mass you have, the more you delay the onset of developing diseases such as diabetes, and heart and circulation problems. The more lean mass you have, the more you will feel like taking exercise and the more stamina you'll have to keep at it – which, in turn, helps to build more lean mass.

An important part of the reason for this is that a mostly

plant-based diet makes your body more alkaline. Every cell in your body has a pH reading, either more acid or alkaline. Our bodies are supposed to be slightly alkaline, but many people these days eat in ways that leave them too acidic. This will drain you of energy, and over the years will lead to the development of serious degenerative diseases.

However, any nutritional information is useless unless you develop a good sense of choice about what you eat. People with a poor sense of their own freedom of choice about food will eat something even though they know it will make them feel ill. They will eat food they don't particularly enjoy, and even food that's gone bad. They feel compelled to do that because of a strong sense of rebellion against their imagined prohibition.

There is no need at all to think in terms of restrictions and prohibitions. Change this attitude, and magic starts to happen. Instead, think in terms of making different choices that produce different outcomes.

If you make regular choices to eat certain kinds of foods, you get a certain kind of outcome: constipation, headaches, feeling bloated or lethargic, for example. If you make different choices, your whole body works better in every way: you become energised, mentally alert and more at peace with yourself. Do you see how there's no need to think in terms of prohibition? The key is to notice which results come from which food choices, and to remember that the next time you are faced with a similar decision.

Perhaps the most common way people deny their freedom of choice is they lock themselves into the assumption (or even worse, commitment) that they will be eating in a healthier way from now on. It's a common dieting mentality, which assumes certain healthy choices are going to be made, with 'No more cream buns for me'. It will help you a great deal not to be too rigid and perfect, as we saw in Chapter 5, and to aim to eat some unhealthy 'food' but just less of it, maybe a lot less. But there's something else here that is truly liberating, and that is to make your choices as you go, and leave your future options wide open with all kinds of possibilities.

All you need to do is choose which outcome you want to create right now. You have a new choice with every encounter with food. In time those choices add up. You will either have made more choices to eat in ways that will age your body faster or in ways that will keep you younger for longer.

Work on changing your thinking in this way, making your choices just for the present time as much as possible. You will be far less likely to procrastinate, to continue to put off making any changes at all, if you leave all future options wide open.

Another part of the difficulty you may encounter with this is that you most likely live in a society that has made addictive overeating seem normal. Did you know, for example, that the same company manufactures Marlboro cigarettes and the products of two of the best-known names in the food industry, Kraft and Nabisco? Think about it. Do you think Philip Morris executives care about your health? Maybe you think that comparing cigarettes with Oreo cookies and Ritz crackers is stretching things a bit, but I want to make an important point. A great many people place a huge and naive degree of trust in the food industry. Look at how much manufactured, processed food you consume, and if it's much more than a few bites here and there, you may be doing just that.

Our language makes it difficult to see, because we simply don't have ways to describe what's happened to the things we eat over the last couple of decades. Even the phrase 'junk food' includes the word 'food'. It's not food, and far from being benign, these products actually do your body harm. They make you ill, very slowly, in much the same way as cigarettes make smokers ill.

Even if you're not so interested in living past 100, the quality of your life is in large part determined by the quality of the food you eat. This, as much as anything else you can do, will determine the length of time you stay in good health, able to do what you want to do, have some independence and be free from pain and disease. It is completely realistic to expect to go through your old age feeling strong and in good health.

You don't need to be confused, because the basics are so well established. To put it all in as short a form as possible:

Eat a balanced and diverse diet, low in calories and high in nutrients. Include three servings of fruit and at least five of vegetables every day. Don't forget pulses and some whole grains. Eat fish twice a week and red meat no more than once a week. Eat a diet low in fat, especially saturated, trans fat and vegetable oils, which are completely unnecessary. Some kinds of fat are essential, and most of us need more omega 3, found in fish and flaxseeds (linseeds). More healthy fats are monounsaturated, such as those found in olive oil and avocados.

A diet primarily based on whole plants provides you with water-soluble fibre for a good digestive system, keeps your blood sugar levels balanced because they have a low glycemic load, deliver antioxidants to neutralise free radical damage, and live enzymes to detoxify the body.

Not only that, but it can be very helpful to know that your body will release storage fat more readily when it's alkaline and when blood sugar levels are balanced.

I do realise that you may have a different opinion about these guidelines on healthy eating, and of course many people have very specific health and dietary issues. The themes in this book are still applicable. What's most important is that you see improvements in your health so that you can stay motivated to eat less.

Food, of course, isn't the only thing that affects aging and health. Genes, degrees of stress and activity, other addictive behaviours, how optimistic or pessimistic you are, and the love and support you live with all play their part.

When it comes to genes, though, your health is only partly determined by the genes you inherit. You may inherit a genetic tendency for a particular disease, but it's poor nutrition that can activate your weakest genetic link.

The only time it's too late to make changes is when you're dead. Assuming you're not dead, you can begin to improve your health and your chances of staying healthy by choosing what you eat on a daily basis, and, perhaps, by becoming more active.

Many people have developed the notion that there's no such thing as 'good' food and 'bad' food. All of it is fine, they say, so long as you don't eat too much of any one thing. This is the way they justify their addictive overeating. Now you know better. See if your idea of a wide variety is in fact a wide variety of sugar, processed grains, fat, salt and animal products; all combined, flavoured and packaged in different ways.

If you don't wake up to the difference between real food and anti-food, you'll find it tough to maintain control of overeating. When you take control, you choose food based on it being good for your health. It's important to enjoy it too, but enjoyment isn't the only consideration. When you eat in an entirely addictive way, enjoyment is your top priority and nutrition barely counts. So choose which way you want to go, and choose the outcome you are willing to live with.

WHAT YOU CAN DO

▸ Are you overweight to the extent that it's considered a health risk or simply in a way that's unfashionable? The latest research indicates that a BMI of 25 for men and 24 for women are the best for health and longevity. Trying to maintain a fashionably skinny body can bring an extra level of difficulty in maintaining control of overeating.

▸ Are you overweight because you aren't active enough, rather than because you eat too much? Even if you eat exactly what you need and no more, you are likely to gain weight if you are inactive. And it's tough to lose weight through eating less alone, without some exercise as well. Energetic walking is often considered the best, and it contributes to building lean mass.

▸ Notice the outcomes you are creating. It's your choice, each time you are going to eat something, and the choices you make have cumulative effects, so that you can feel better and better (or worse and worse) over time. If you continue to appreciate the better health, you will lose weight, assuming you're overweight to start with. But you'll be achieving it in a way that's much more empowering and sustainable.

▸ Educate yourself. There are outcomes of food choices that

you may not be aware of until it's too late. For example, vegetable oils damage cell membranes, making every cell in the body less efficient. Trans fats (hydrogenated oils) are well known to wreak all kinds of havoc in the body.

▸ When making choices, know that sugar drains nutrients from the body, so think of sugar as the opposite of a vitamin pill. The single best thing you can do for your health may be to reduce your sugar intake. In many ways, your body regards refined carbohydrates as sugar, so white rice, refined cereals and breads have many similar effects as table sugar and glucose syrup.

▸ If chocolate is your thing, have you thought about improving the quality of what you buy? Chocolate itself can be beneficial, but not when relatively small amounts are mixed together with very poor quality fats and refined sugar, as is the case with most popular commercial bars and sweets. You could accept your addictive desire for the endless fixes of flavoured, sugary fat and save your money for more occasional, top-quality brands with a much higher percentage of (dark) chocolate.

It's not nearly as addictive, so you will find it easier to control. This also means your preference is likely to be for the higher fat and sugar versions – which has nothing to do with chocolate itself.

RUBY'S STORY

I'm an accountant, not a writer, so I hope this makes sense. I still want to lose weight but these are the benefits I'm getting right now and I can hardly believe how thrilled and excited I am with them. Weight loss is great but it's certainly not the whole picture any more, not even the biggest part of it.

Better skin condition

No more frequent sore throats due to a weak immune system

Ability to breathe easily

Less risk of a heart attack or cancer

Less risk of varicose veins, which runs in my family

No more hair loss due to poor nutrition

Feel like a cat (all stretched and supple) when I wake up, instead of bloated

No more shame (that inability to look the shopkeeper in the eye when I buy sweets)

No more hiding what and how much I eat

No more roller coaster eating and the emotions attached to it

I can eat sweets if I want to, any time and any amount, they will still be there tomorrow and the diet doesn't start then

No more fear of going out with friends because it might ruin my diet

No more boring my friends with my weight problems and diet stories

I can stare down a cookie
I control food, it doesn't control me; the invisible monster really
doesn't exist
No more waking up every morning in a state of fear and panic,
wondering if I'm going to stick to my diet that day

I noticed an interesting justification this morning. I woke up and
decided that since it's my birthday, I'll have cookies and tea to
celebrate. This was at 6am in the morning. Then I realised that I
don't have to justify it! I decided it's fine, reached for the cookie
jar and suddenly didn't feel like it. This is probably my first
birthday ever that I am not stuffing my face with cake!

There was a box of chocolates in the office the whole day. I
decided to eat four, had them, enjoyed them, and the box never
bothered me for the rest of the day.

[Ruby wrote this for the first edition of this book, soon after she
attended one of my seminars. She emailed six years later: 'My
eating is still under control. I overeat sometimes but I would say
it is less than 10% of the time. And to be honest when it happens
I'm not even too worried. I've kept off the 35 pounds, without
any dieting.']

CHAPTER EIGHT

STAYING AHEAD OF THE GAME

Imagine you live in a world where some food will keep you healthy and some will make you ill, and everybody seems not to know which is which. Imagine that intelligent and creative people are paid good money to convince you to eat the food that will make you ill. Imagine that everyone you know eats it and pretends it's good for them. Imagine you live in a world where the best way to get though a day is with the least amount of physical effort. Imagine that children are taught that the best way to honour themselves is through impressing others; that the most important thing in life is to look good at any cost.

It doesn't matter if you don't have much of an imagination, because in one way or another you already live in this world. To better understand the impact our environment has on us, let's look at the many examples of people whose culture changed quite dramatically.

The best example may be the people of the Western Samoa Islands in the Pacific. A couple of generations ago they were still fairly isolated from the rest of the world, living in more natural ways and eating food grown locally. The discovery of valuable natural resources created enormous wealth, and the Islanders now have one of the highest per capita incomes in the world. They have also become the most obese nation in the world.

Their wealth has meant that they can now be much less active. It has also attracted the Western food industry, so that the traditional diet of fish, vegetables and fruit has been replaced by manufactured, processed food. More than three-quarters of their population became obese and one third diabetic.

There are similar examples of people who moved from one culture to another. In their traditional culture, the Japanese have the lowest rates of heart disease and are among the longest-lived people in the world. Those who migrate to America, though, become overweight and get heart disease just as much as other Americans. Similar comparisons have been made between Afro-Americans and their African relatives.

Another example can be found in the experience of a group of American Indians. The Pima Indians of Arizona lived and farmed on the land as their ancestors did, up until the 1980s when they were granted a casino concession and became extremely wealthy. They now live a comfortable American lifestyle, and eat a more American diet. They became well known as the most obese group of people in the United States.

Their wealth means the Pimas can afford the best hospitals - and they need them. Their excess weight has lead to high blood pressure, bone, muscle and joint strains and many kinds of cancer. More than half of them have become diabetic.

For their genetic cousins, another group of Pimas who live in Mexico, diabetes and obesity are virtually unknown. Mexican Pimas spend much of their time in physical labour on the land, eating a diet high in vegetable fibre and low in fat.

These examples show clearly the impact of our modern culture, with its constant supply of attractive but toxic food, on weight and health. But this is not intended to leave you in a state of gloom and doom about being able to make changes without emigrating to the North Pole.

First of all, it shows you that genes are not solely responsible for overeating, because genes don't change that fast. Second, it's less likely that unresolved emotional trauma is the main cause either. It's not likely that a more affluent culture made so many people less capable of dealing with their emotions, or with deep emotional scars in need of healing. What makes much more sense is having easy access to enormous quantities and varieties of highly addictive rubbish to eat. These days we are surrounded by it.

There was just one brand and variety of potato crisp when I

was a child in the 1950's. Now there's a whole aisle in each supermarket devoted to different kinds. Let's not blame the supermarkets, either, because the only reason they are on sale is because people buy them. It's marketed to you, you buy it, it's hugely lucrative, so people manufacture and market more of it. You are an active link in that chain, not a victim of it. It's possible to walk down those aisles and not put that stuff in your trolley!

A good principle to remember is that if it's advertised and marketed, it's addictive. Anything addictive sells itself; which is why sugar, salt, processed grains and fat are included in these processed foods.

Not only has our culture accepted unhealthy food as the norm, but at the same time slimness has been promoted as the ideal, especially for women. The message is that if you're slim you're a good person and if you're overweight you don't count. Even when health issues are acknowledged, it's far more common to talk about a 'weight problem' rather than an 'eating problem', keeping you totally focused on that one effect.

When all you care about is weight, it can be tough to stay motivated because weight loss is so slow. Perhaps your first waking thought is the realisation of how overweight you still are, and this sense of failure before you've even begun your day can undermine any motivation you may have had. You think that maybe you'll make it through another day in control, if you're lucky, but even if you do you'll still be overweight.

It makes a big difference to keep in mind those benefits that give you more immediate feedback. The more you can identify them, the more you can stay motivated in the short and the long term. It's not that weight ever becomes something that doesn't matter at all. Of course it matters and will continue to matter to the vast majority of us. It's just that you include other kinds of motivation, so that appearance isn't the only thing; preferably, not even the most important thing.

There's a paradox in this: the more you can let go of wanting to lose weight, the more likely it is to happen – assuming you can find other good reasons to eat less. The challenge for many people is to get as interested in eating to support their health as they already are in 'looking good'. Focus on healthier eating, and once you've lost the weight you'll have reasons to maintain it. You'll need those good reasons because some temptation will be there, no matter what you weigh.

An addictive relationship with food isn't something that goes away completely, but it is something you can learn to deal with so that it becomes much less of a problem. Most people try to control their eating by trying to avoid temptation. This is fine up to a point, but it usually means that you never learn how to deal with your addictive desire to eat, so you're almost guaranteed to return to overeating.

This doesn't mean you're a hopeless failure; it just means that you haven't yet developed the skill of dealing with your addictive desire. Maybe you didn't know how to do that before you came across this book, but now you do. You allow yourself to feel it; you become willing to accept that uncomfortable, unsatisfied feeling because it's the way you stop eating so much.

I do know this isn't an easy thing to do. Let's face it, if it was, more people would be happy with their eating, their health and their weight, wouldn't they? The thing to remember is that it gets easier in time if it's handled correctly, which is what this book is all about. But at first, there really is significant conflict to work through, and nobody can ever do that for you. However, it is do-able.

The challenge of facing up to your addictive desire will take up time, effort and energy. But balance this against the years of difficulties that you may have been living with for some time – let alone the potential problems that could lie ahead, such as surgery or poor health. At first it could feel like being stuck between a rock and a hard place. Please know that the hard place does become softer!

A genuine feeling of free choice is essential, so keep reminding yourself you don't have to do any of this. You can continue to overeat all your life. It's when you deny that freedom that you'll find yourself hoovering up everything in sight, always fearing this will be your last meal, or your last overindulgent meal. When food is forbidden you've absolutely got to eat it now because this may be your last chance.

Very many people deny choice because they are afraid of it. So they think in terms of commitment, perfectionism and projection. It's entirely possible to comply with this sense of restriction for a while, but eventually it leads to rebellion in some form; either overeating again or perhaps another addictive behaviour. Eventually it becomes almost impossible to get yourself back into that self-imposed state of deprivation again.

You turn this on its head by letting yourself know you can eat whatever food you want – and you don't have to do it to prove it! You can always come back tomorrow and have some more. This food, or something like it, is going to be available to you and you can have it every day, for breakfast, lunch and dinner and snacks in between. Just remember the complete picture of what you're choosing: the downside as well as the upside. Be honest about it if you choose food that is not at all good for your health.

As much as you possibly can, buy your food in its original packaging, the one that was designed hundreds of generations ago. Follow nutritional advice and a reasonable exercise programme, and you will of course get results. You can turn around most signs of ill health you already have. And if you are already in the best of health you can take preventative measures, being active rather than passive in maintaining your good health. Think holistically, in that wherever you start to make changes, results appear on each level of body, mind and spirit.

It makes sense to me that addictive behaviour is related to all three of these realms: physical, mental and spiritual. To say, as many people do, that addiction arises from a problem in one of these is to ignore the other two. The role of the mind is often forgotten, but as you've seen in these pages and hopefully experienced in your own life, the mind is key in taking control of addictive overeating.

WHAT YOU CAN DO

▶ Dip into this book from time to time to remind yourself of things you've discovered here. You might want to mark passages or write notes for yourself in a journal.

▶ Stay involved. Most things in life require maintenance. You don't go to work just one time to have a career. And you don't speak to someone just once in order to have a relationship with them. Why should your relationship with food be any different?

You've now discovered the ways of thinking that get you stuck, traps that mean you are unable to make lasting changes in your eating habits. It's not that you don't fall into these traps ever again, it's that you learn the skill of getting out of them fast. You get skilled at readjusting your frame of mind.

▸ Take care not to take things for granted. When you've made some changes, these changes become normal and you can forget how things were before those changes were made.

▸ Whenever you see models in magazines or beauty shows remember that they weigh less than the clinical criteria for anorexia nervosa. Many (perhaps most) have eating disorders which means that food is a source of distress for them.

▸ If you are a parent, please note that this book is written for adults, and not for children. It may not be wise to expect children to make adult choices as children's brains aren't capable and nor should they be. Children need to have some choices made for them and good role models to follow.

SALLY'S STORY

I'm 39, I'm married and I have always worked as a fashion buyer, which I absolutely love. I used to diet a lot when I was in my teens and twenties and that seemed to work quite well, but over the last ten years or so I found it impossible to diet and I ended up feeling rather despondent about it all. I thought that the 'Eating Less' seminar would help me to get back to dieting again, but I think it's been better than that.

This seminar to me was proof to me that I could do

something I always had wanted: to make some kind of change so that dieting became unnecessary. I always knew it was a mind thing as much as anything else, but the seminar helped me to see a lot of things more clearly. In particular, looking at the problem of these two incompatible things: knowing you want to eat better, to eat more fruit and vegetables, and you're absolutely convinced in your mind that you'd feel so much fitter and better, and then half an hour later you're eating the wrong thing. Just because you've just got to have that slice of cake or whatever.

Resolving the conflict between this is something most people don't even begin to do. It's about knowing that by eating better you're actually taking care of yourself. That for me was the essence of the seminar. I do eat much better now, and especially I eat more fruit and vegetables.

I've learned to deal with all the comments about the lost weight, but people seem to have settled about it now and I can just carry on in peace. Although I am aware that I need to keep making an effort with regard to what and when I eat, and although I am sometimes more successful than others, I've really stopped seeing food as anything other than my friend, which is a breath of fresh air!

I go through phases where I eat nothing but fruit until the late afternoon and that works well for me. I wouldn't have been able to do that before I did the seminar. I go though quite long periods of not eating wheat. It goes in phases. I'm more in tune with what food does to my body now. If I snack on bread and honey I'll get very sleepy half an hour later, and a big meal at lunchtime will do the same thing. I feel bloated after I eat white bread.

I hardly ever eat chocolate now because I don't really enjoy it nearly as much as I think I will. Every now and then I go and buy a chocolate bar, maybe once every few months, and I think 'I want it, so I'm going to have it'. But then I eat it and I think that wasn't such a big deal. I don't feel guilty about it. I think I'm less hung-up on food now, which is very nice.

FURTHER HELP

For current details of products and services that support the material in this book, visit www.eatingless.com.

BOOKS BY GILLIAN RILEY

Eating Less: Say Goodbye to Overeating
Random House UK/Vermilion (1998, 2005)
The full version, containing more information on research, written exercises to help integrate these ideas and more detailed instructions on techniques.

How To Stop Smoking And Stay Stopped For Good
Random House UK/Vermilion (1992, 1997, 2007)
Stopping smoking can be an important part of the process for some of those who overeat. Overeating issues don't get fully addressed while smoking continues.

Willpower!
Random House UK/Vermilion (2003)
Covers similar material, but includes general discussions about addictive behaviours, current thinking and research.

Quitting Smoking
Gill & Macmillan/Newleaf (2001)
The short, easy-read, pocket book version.

All of these books are available through bookshops and online booksellers.